PRACTICE TEST PAPERS

Sarah Sheepy

Contents

Introduction

Instructions on using the Practice Test Papers

Understanding Assessment

What is assessment?
Teacher assessment will form the main part of your child's result at the end of Key Stage 1 (at the age of 7). However, tests and tasks help to validate the teacher's own assessment.

What are the children tested on?
All children study the National Curriculum from Year 1. At the end of Year 2, the tests will assess your child's knowledge, skills and understanding in the programmes of study that they have followed from Year 1.

What tests will my child take?
Teacher assessment for seven-year-olds covers:

- reading
- writing
- speaking and listening
- maths
- science

These assessments take account of how your child performed in Key Stage 1 tasks and tests. The tasks and tests cover:

- reading
- writing (including handwriting and spelling)
- maths

The tasks and tests are informal and can be taken at a time the school chooses, although they usually take place towards the end of Year 2. The tasks and tests last for less than three hours altogether and the results help to inform the teacher's overall assessment of your child. No statutory testing is carried out at Key Stage 1.

What do the maths tests assess in my child?
In maths the programme of study covers four areas or attainment targets:
Mathematics 1: Using and applying mathematics
Mathematics 2: Number
Mathematics 3: Space, shape and measures
Mathematics 4: Handling data

At Key Stage 1, the focus is on Number and Space, shape and measures.

Can my child fail a test?
It is important that children understand they are not going to 'pass' or 'fail' the test – it will just show what they have learned and what they can do.

Preparing your Child for Tests

These practice test papers are designed to prepare your child for school tests by giving them the confidence of knowing the sort of questions they will experience.

How will these practice test papers help?
These practice test papers will help you to assess how your child is doing at school. They will give you an indication of your child's strengths and weaknesses and how you can help them.

How can you improve your child's score?
- Mark the papers.
- Look at what your child got wrong and talk it through with them.
- Let your child do the test again.
- Remember – keep practising the things they get wrong. For example, if they find subtraction difficult, give them plenty of practice.
- Try to encourage your child not to throw away marks, by reading a question carefully and checking their answer.

About these Practice Test Papers

In this book there are three sets of papers for completion.

Test Paper A – Levels 1–2	(30 marks)
Test Paper B – Level 3	(30 marks)
Test Paper C – Level 3	(30 marks)

Using the Tests

Maths
Sets A, B and C are three different tests.

First of all, give your child Test Paper A (Levels 1–2).

Remind them of the following:
- Read the questions carefully.
- Check your answers.

Your child cannot be given any help with reading mathematical words he or she does not know.

The test has to be all your child's own work.

When they have finished, mark the paper.

Look at the tables on pages 5–6 to find out what level your child has achieved.

Marking the Tests and Assessing Levels

1. Marking the test papers is quite simple. Just use the pull-out Answers and Mark Scheme found on pages 65–72.
2. Make sure your child has completed the relevant test.
3. Add up the marks on the paper. Each test is marked out of 30.
4. Write the marks in the corresponding table below.

	Paper A	Paper B	Paper C
Score (out of 30)			

Paper A
Add up your child's total score for the test out of the maximum of 30 marks. Then refer to the table below to find the level and grade.

Number of marks	0–4	5–6	7–12	13–18	19–30
Level	No level	Level 1	Level 2c	Level 2b	Level 2a

If your child achieved Level 2a in Test Paper A, then they can try either or both of the Level 3 papers.

Papers B and C
Add up your child's total score for the test out of the maximum of 30 marks. Then refer to the table below to find whether they have achieved Level 3.

Number of marks	0–12	13–30
Level	Level 3 not achieved	Level 3 achieved

In school your child would only take one Level 3 paper. However, two tests are provided here for additional practice at home.

Please note: these tests are only a guide to the level your child can achieve and cannot guarantee the same level is achieved during Key Stage 1.

How well has my child done in these tests?

The results show whether or not your child has reached the expected National Curriculum level at the age of 7.

Level	Aged 7
Level 1	Below average
Level 2 Level 2c Level 2b Level 2a	At level expected
Level 3	Excellent
Level 4	Exceptional
Level 5	
Level 6	
Level 7	
Level 8	

What do the levels mean?

When your child's maths paper is marked, the correct marks are collated to give your child an overall score. This score is then matched to a National Curriculum level.

The government target for pupils at the end of Year 2 is to achieve Level 2. Some pupils will be working below this level and achieve Level 1, whilst other pupils will be working above the expected level and achieve Level 3.

Test Paper A

Instructions:

- find a quiet place where you can sit down and complete the test paper undisturbed
- an adult will need to read the first 5 questions to you
- make sure you have all the necessary equipment to complete the test paper (a pencil, rubber and ruler)
- read the questions carefully
- answer all the questions in this paper
- go through and check your answers when you have finished the test paper

Time:

Take as long as necessary to complete the test paper but aim to complete it within 1 hour. Take a break halfway through.

Note to Parents:

Check how your child has done using pages 65–66 of the Answers and Mark Scheme.

Test Paper A

Page	9	11	13	15	17	19	21	22	Max. Mark	**Actual Mark**
Score	....	....	....	....	....	....	....	....	30	....

First name ....

Last name ....

KEY STAGE 1
Levels 1–2

Test Paper A

Maths

Test Paper A

Read out these questions carefully to your child. Explain that they should listen to you and then write the answers on the opposite page.

1 What number is 7 less than 15? **Write your answer in box a.**

2 There are 4 tables in the classroom. 5 children sit at each table. How many children are there altogether? **Write your answer in box b.**

3 Look at the shapes. All but one of the shapes are triangles.
Circle the shape that is not a triangle.

4 **Circle the calculation that gives the answer 4.**

5 **Tick the scales which show $2\frac{1}{2}$ kg.**

Now continue with the rest of the paper on your own.

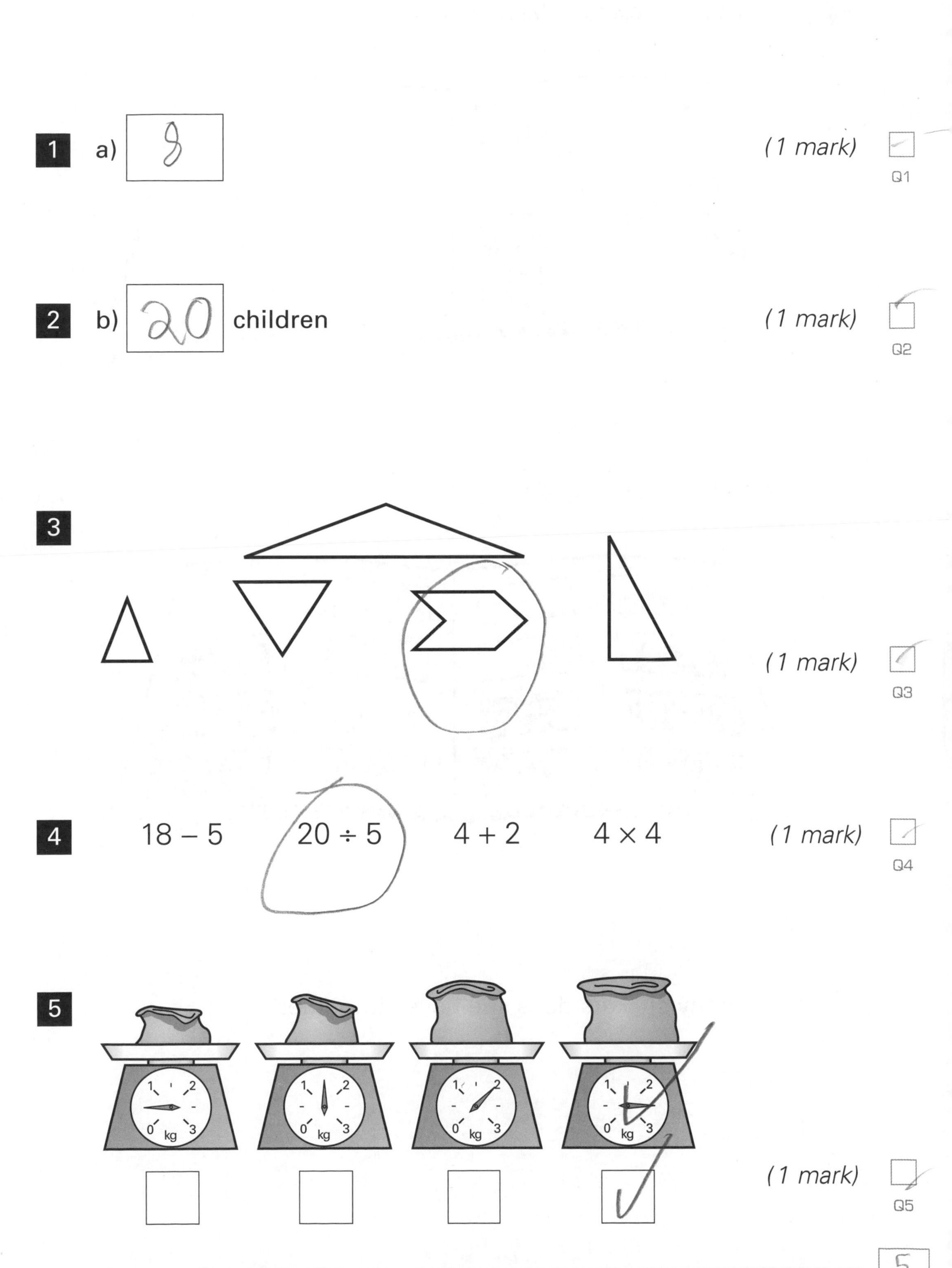
1 a) 8 (1 mark) Q1
2 b) 20 children (1 mark) Q2
3 (1 mark) Q3
4 18 – 5 20 ÷ 5 4 + 2 4 × 4 (1 mark) Q4
5 (1 mark) Q5
1 2 0 kg 3
5 subtotal

6 There are 8 stickers in Mia's book.

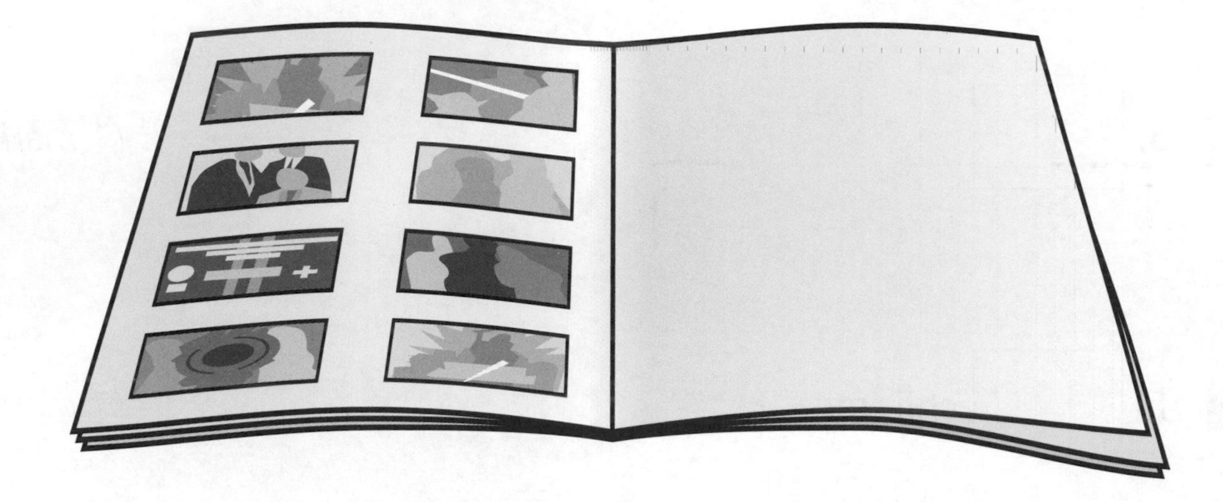

She adds another 6 stickers.

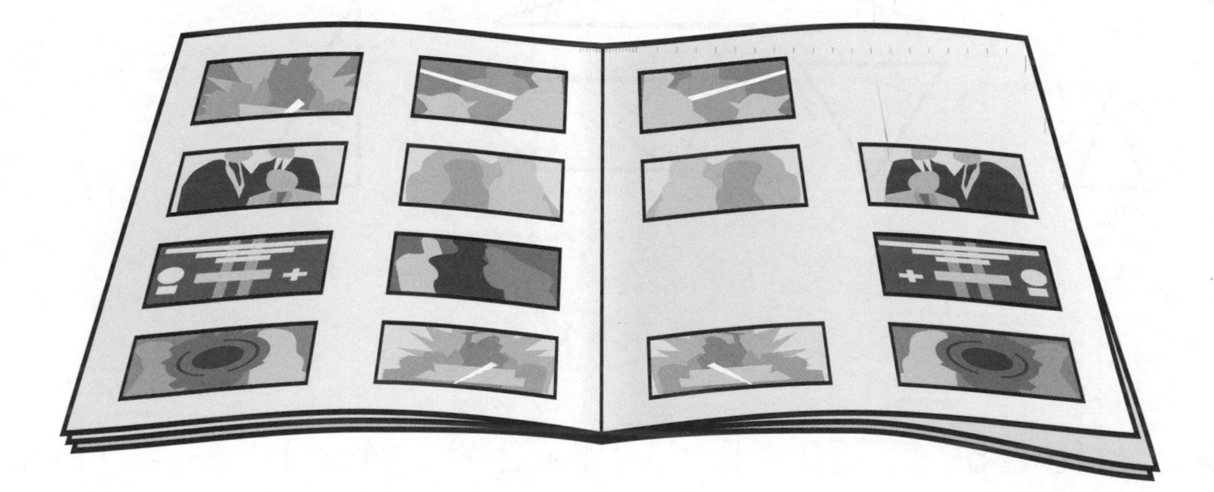

How many stickers does she have altogether?

stickers *(1 mark)*

Q6

7 Tick (✔) the shape with 2 **short** sides and 2 **long** sides.

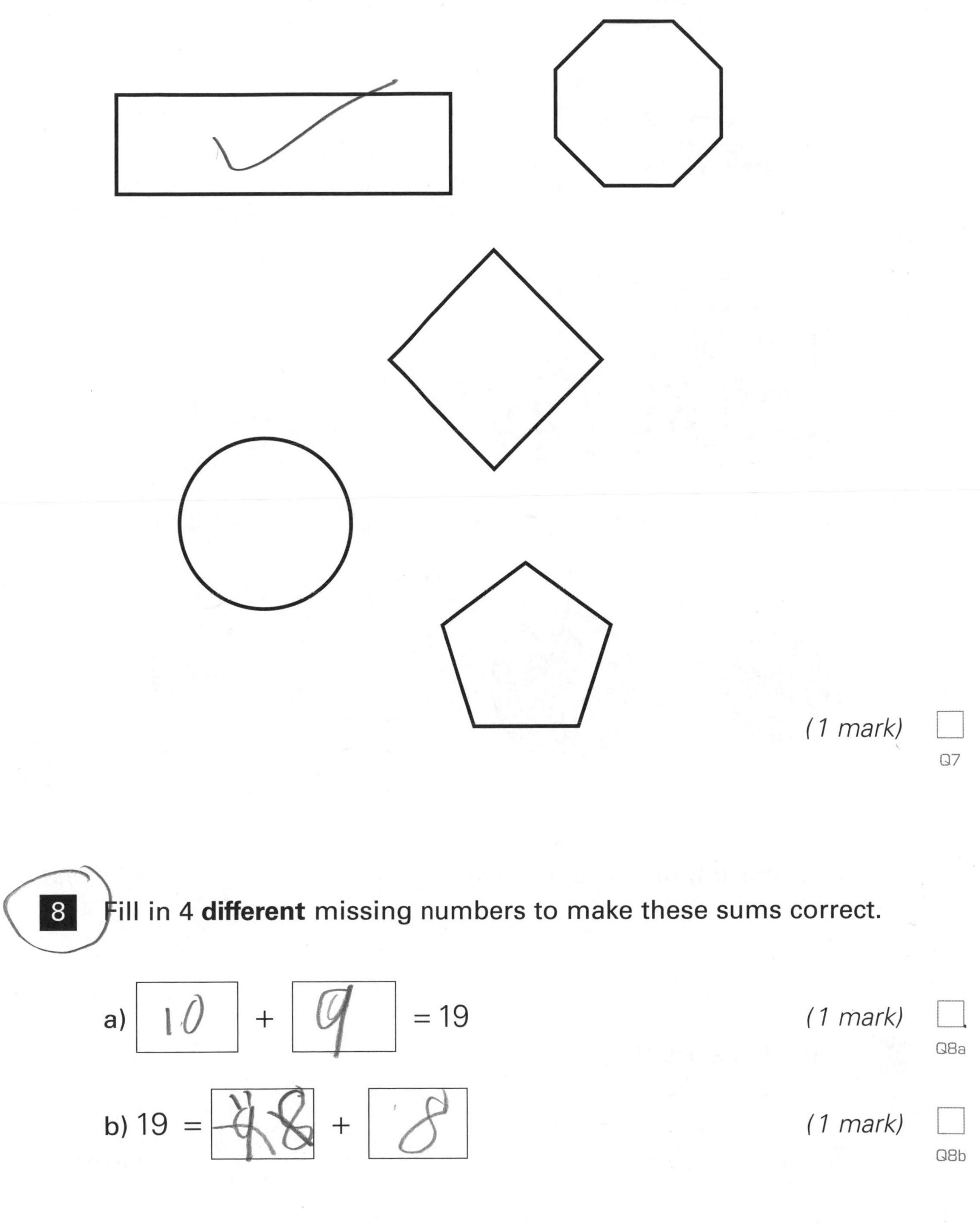

(1 mark) Q7

8 Fill in 4 **different** missing numbers to make these sums correct.

a) ☐ + ☐ = 19 *(1 mark)* Q8a

b) 19 = ☐ + ☐ *(1 mark)* Q8b

subtotal

9 David wants to buy a carton of milk.

He has 15p.

How much **more** does he need? 

p *(1 mark)* Q9

Write the answer.

$8 + 4 + 7 + 3 =$ 22 *(1 mark)* Q10

11 Write numbers in the boxes to make this sum correct.

2	3	=	3	7	−	1	4

(1 mark) Q11

12 There are 10 satsumas in each bag and 7 more.

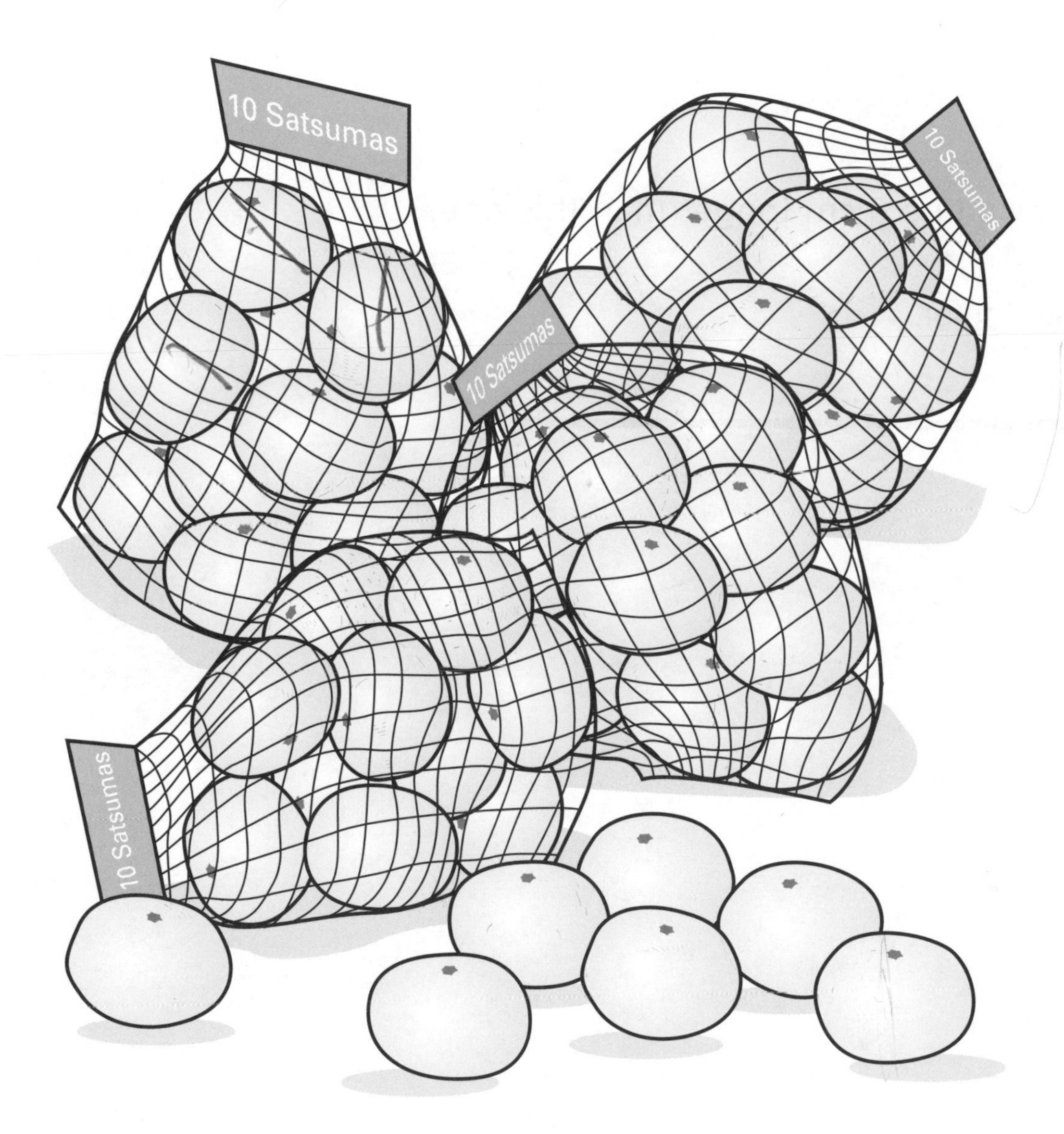

How many satsumas are there altogether?

47	satsumas

(1 mark) Q12

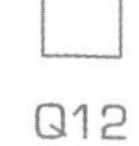
subtotal

13 Write the missing numbers in the sequence.

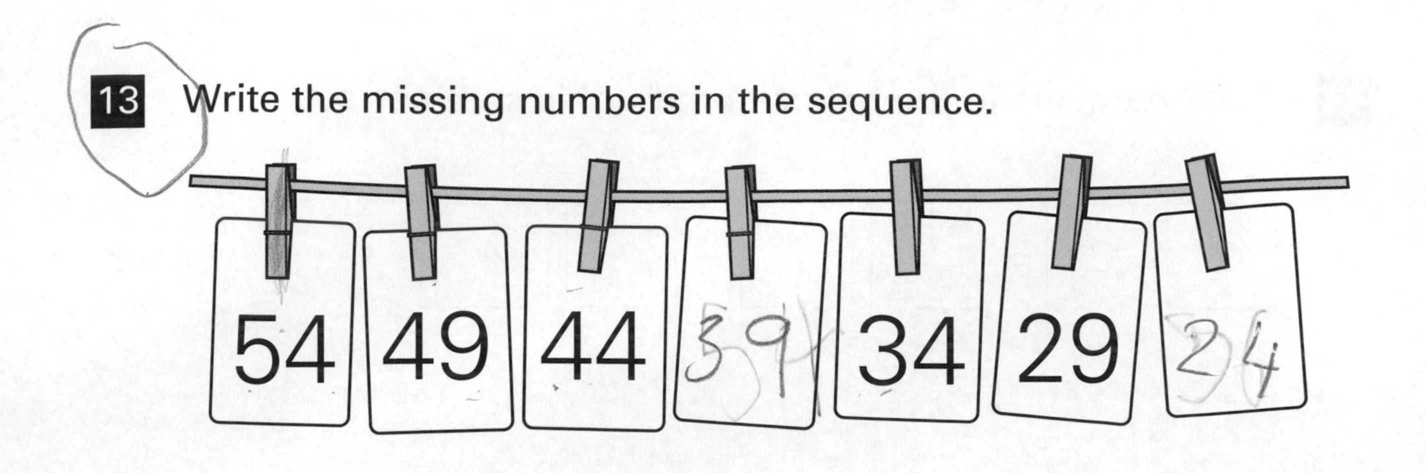

(1 mark)

Q13

14 Draw a line 6 cm longer than this one.

Use a ruler.

(1 mark)

Q14

15 The 2 numbers joined together have a difference of 8.

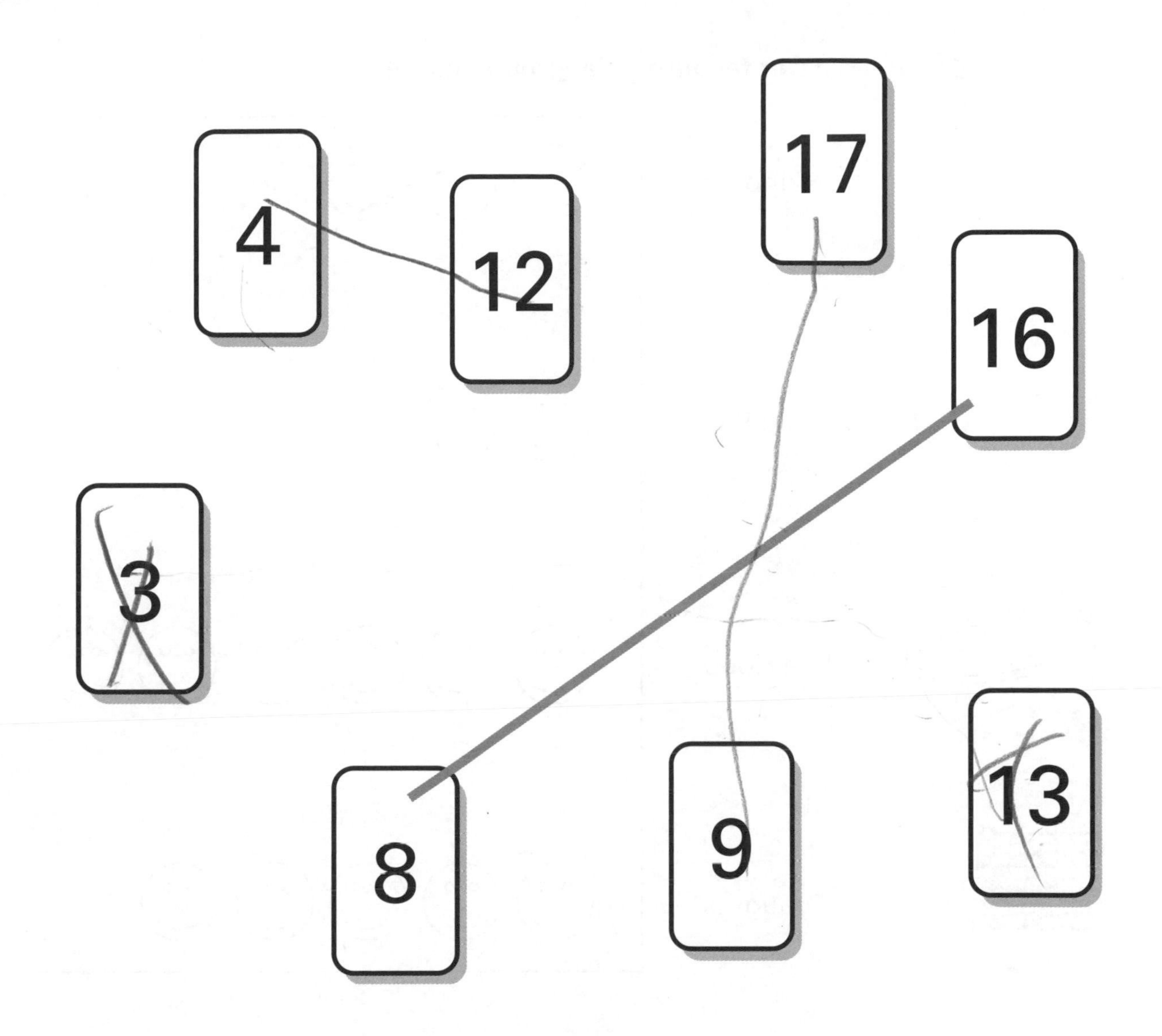

Join 2 other numbers together that have a difference of 8. *(1 mark)*

Q15

16 Some of these numbers can be divided exactly by 10.

12 40 35 28 10 36 90

Draw a circle around all the numbers which can be divided exactly by 10. *(1 mark)*

Q16

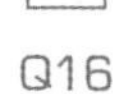

17 Some children made a chart.

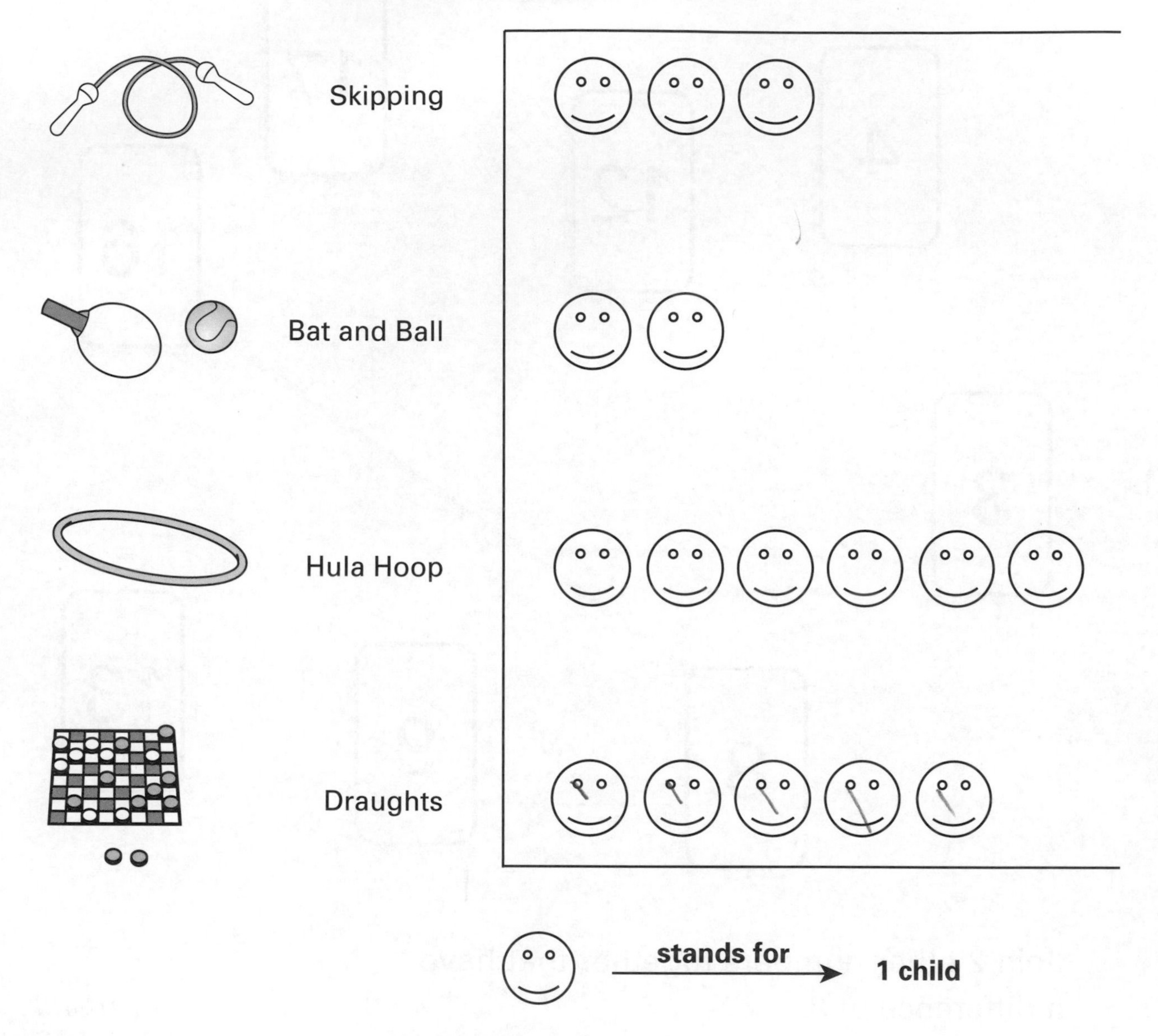

How many more children chose draughts than bat and ball?

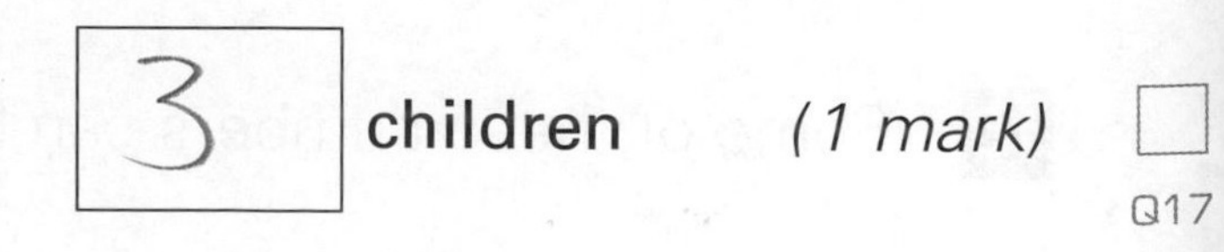

18 Put a ring around the **smallest** number.

108 199 198 103 133 183 *(1 mark)*

Q18

19

Draw the other 2 sides of this rectangle.

Use a ruler. *(1 mark)*

Q19

subtotal

20 James has 37p.

a) How many marbles can he buy? 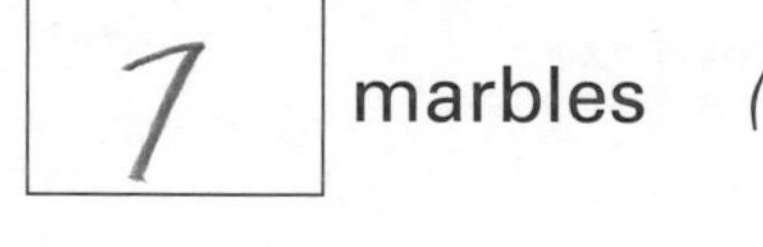 7 marbles *(1 mark)* Q20a

b) How much money will he have left?  2 p *(1 mark)* Q20b

21 Write the answer.

13 + 8 = 9 + 12 *(1 mark)* Q21

12 + 9

22 Joel scored 9 in a game of darts.

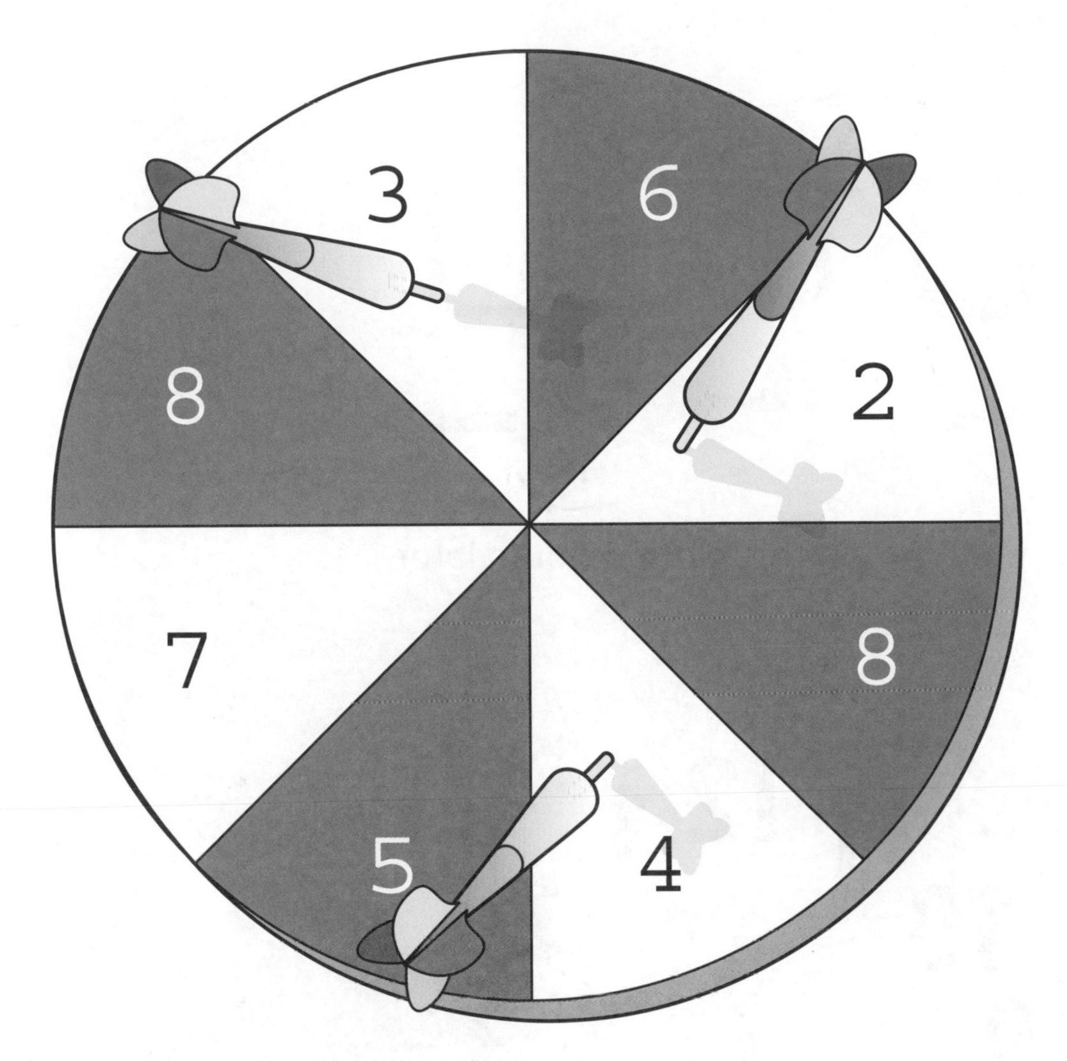

Chloe scored **double** Joel's score.

What score did Chloe get? [18] *(1 mark)* Q22

23 **Complete the sequences.**

a) 1 5 9 [13] 17 [21] 25 *(1 mark)* Q23a

b) 26 22 [18] [14] 10 [6] 2 *(1 mark)* Q23b

 subtotal

24 Look at this clock.

Show the time on this clock 2 hours later.

(1 mark) Q24

25 Write the number which is 12 **less than** 50. 38 *(1 mark)* Q25

26 There are 25 people on a bus. At the next stop 8 people get off.

How many people are left on the bus?

 **people** *(1 mark)*

Q26

subtotal

27

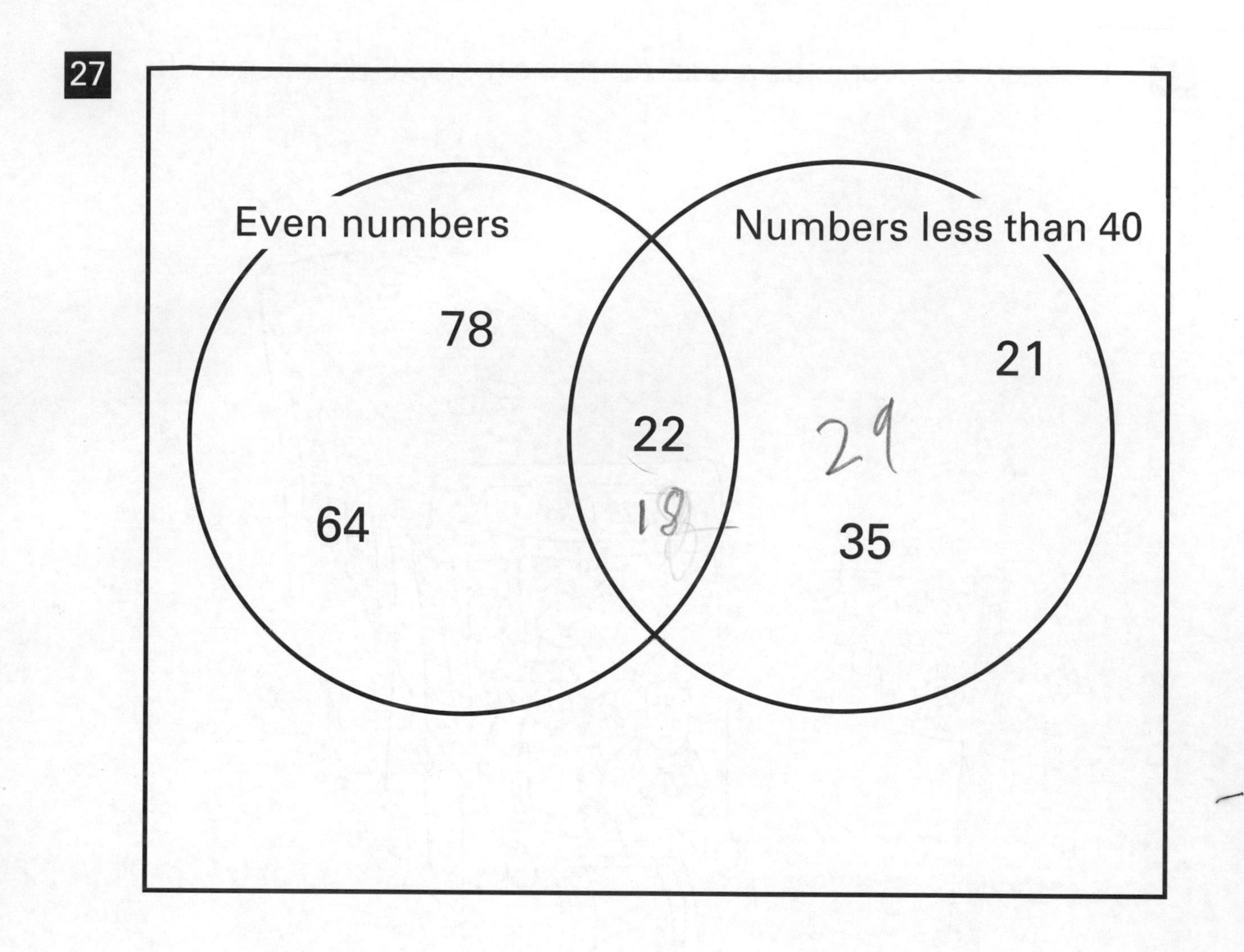

Write these 2 numbers in the Venn diagram.

18 29

(1 mark)

Q27

END OF TEST

subtotal

KEY STAGE 1
Level 3
Test Paper B

Maths

Test Paper B

Instructions:

- find a quiet place where you can sit down and complete the test paper undisturbed
- an adult will need to read the first 5 questions to you
- make sure you have all the necessary equipment to complete the test paper (a pencil, rubber, ruler and small mirror)
- read the questions carefully
- answer all the questions in this paper
- go through and check your answers when you have finished the test paper

Time:

Take as long as necessary to complete the test paper but aim to complete it within 1 hour. Take a break halfway through.

Note to Parents:

Check how your child has done using pages 67–68 of the Answers and Mark Scheme.

Test Paper B

Test Paper B

Page	25	27	29	31	33	35	37	39	41	42	Max. Mark	**Actual Mark**
Score	....	....	....	....	....	....	....	....	....	....	30	....

First name ....

Last name ....

Read out these questions carefully to your child. Explain that they should listen to you and then write the answers on the opposite page.

1 A pair of jeans costs £18. A coat costs £23 more.
How much does the coat cost? **Write your answer in box a.**

2 2 numbers are multiplied together to make 180.
Which 2 numbers could be multiplied together? **Write your 2 numbers in boxes b and c.**

3 A cuboid has 3 red faces and 1 blue face. The other faces are all yellow. How many faces of the cuboid are yellow? **Write your answer in box d.**

4 Write the number one thousand and ninety four. **Write it in box e.**

5 **Circle the units you would use to measure your weight.**

Now continue with the rest of the paper on your own.

1 a) £ [81] *(1 mark)* Q1

2 b) [90] ✗ c) [2] *(1 mark)* Q2

3 d) [2] faces *(1 mark)* Q3

4 e) [1094] *(1 mark)* Q4

5 kilometres millimetres minutes

kilograms litres *(1 mark)* Q5

subtotal

6 Here are some signs.

Write a sign in each box to make this correct.

140 ☐ 2 ☐ 70 *(1 mark)*

Q6

7 **How many 5p pieces are there in £1.50?**

☐ 5p pieces *(1 mark)*

Q7

8 Look at these amounts. **Place them in order in the boxes below.**

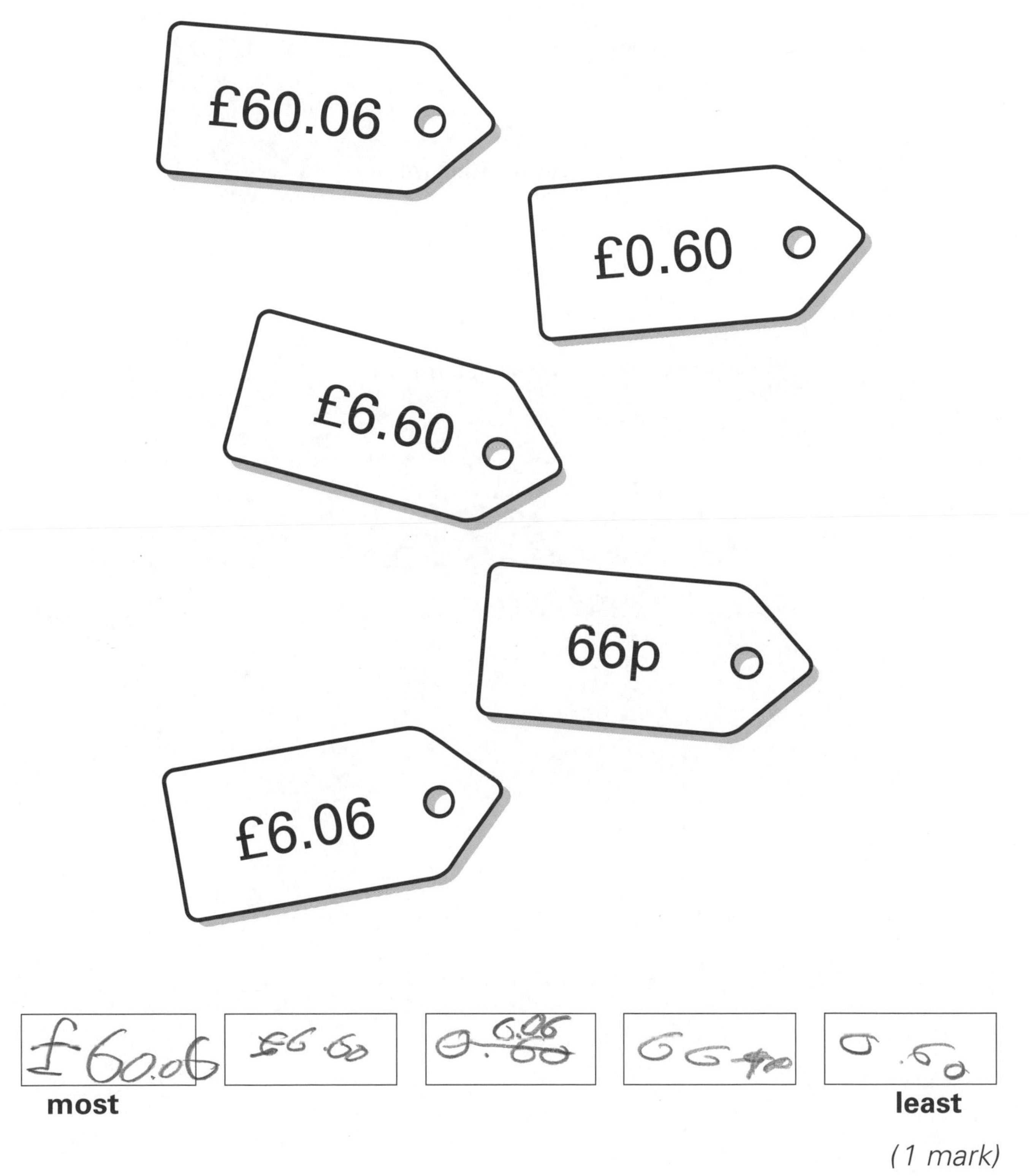

£60.06	£6.60	6.06	66p	0.60

most **least**

(1 mark)

Q8

subtotal

9 Shade this container to show 250 ml.

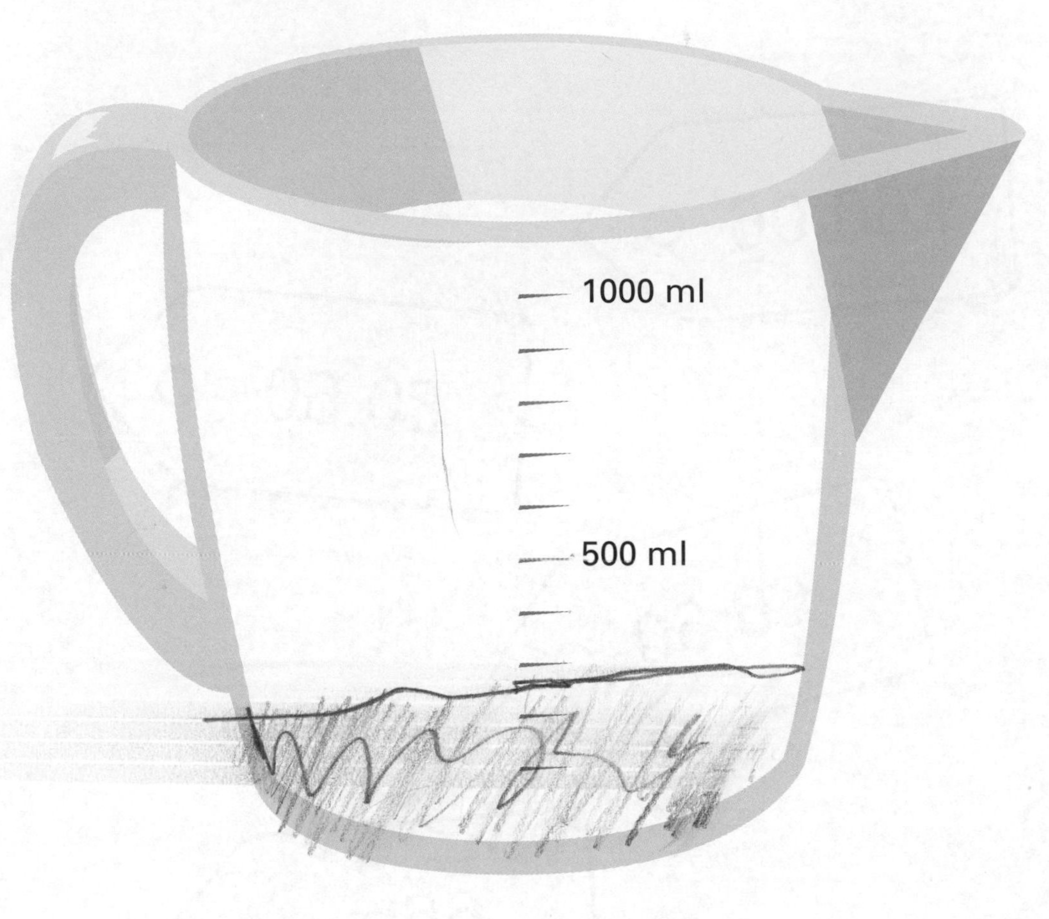

(1 mark)

Q9

10

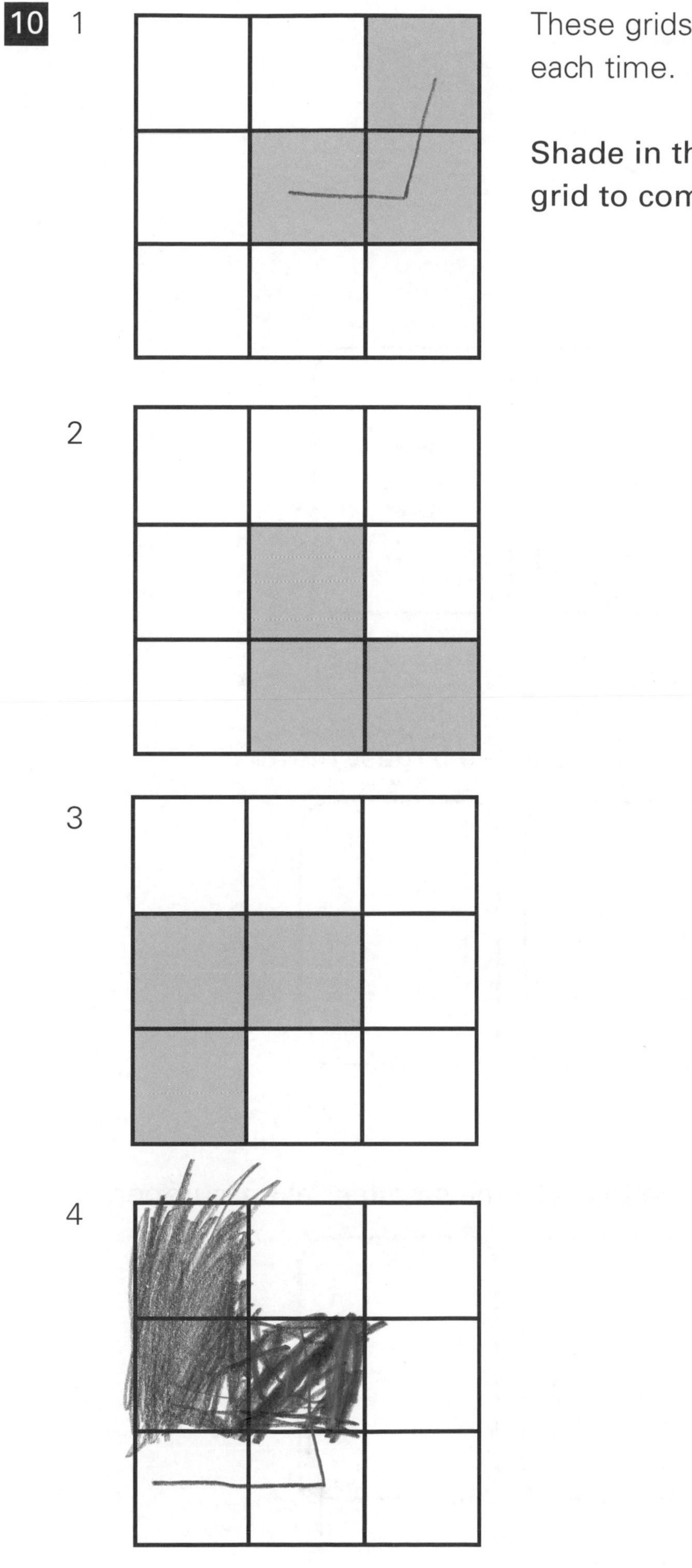

These grids are turned by a $\frac{1}{4}$ turn each time.

Shade in the squares in the last grid to complete the pattern.

(1 mark)

Q10

subtotal

11 Write the total.

74 + 116 = 190 *(1 mark)*

Q11

12 Look at these cards.

6 7 5

a) Use each card **once** to make the **largest** number.

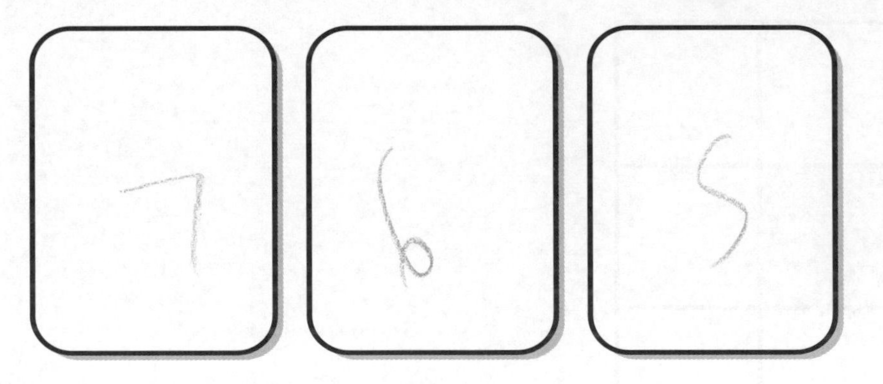

(1 mark)

Q12a

b) Use each card **once** to make the **smallest even** number.

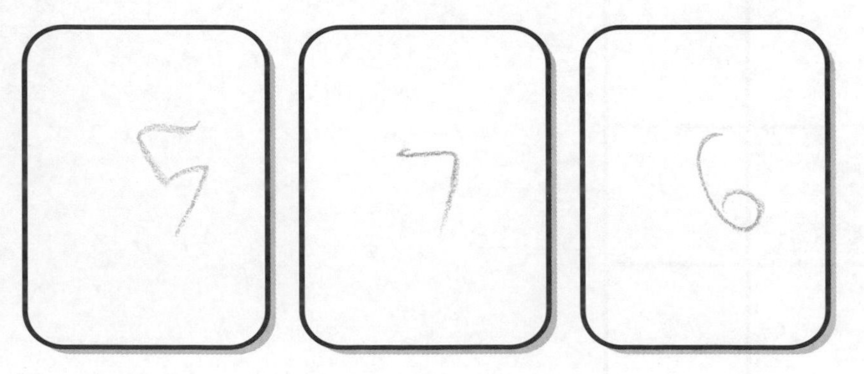

(1 mark)

Q12b

13 George's baby bottle contains 100 ml of juice.

100
- 25

If he drinks $\frac{1}{4}$ of it, how much is left?

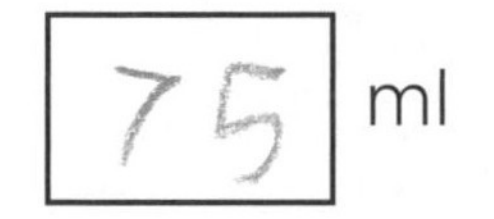

ml

(1 mark)

Q13

subtotal

14

Spelling test results: Red group (marks out of 50)	
Javed	48
Chloe	32
Helen	24
Meera	39
Peter	43
Jilly	46
David	21

The children's spelling test results are shown on a bar chart. They received 1 mark for each correct spelling, but 2 scores have been mixed up in the bar chart.

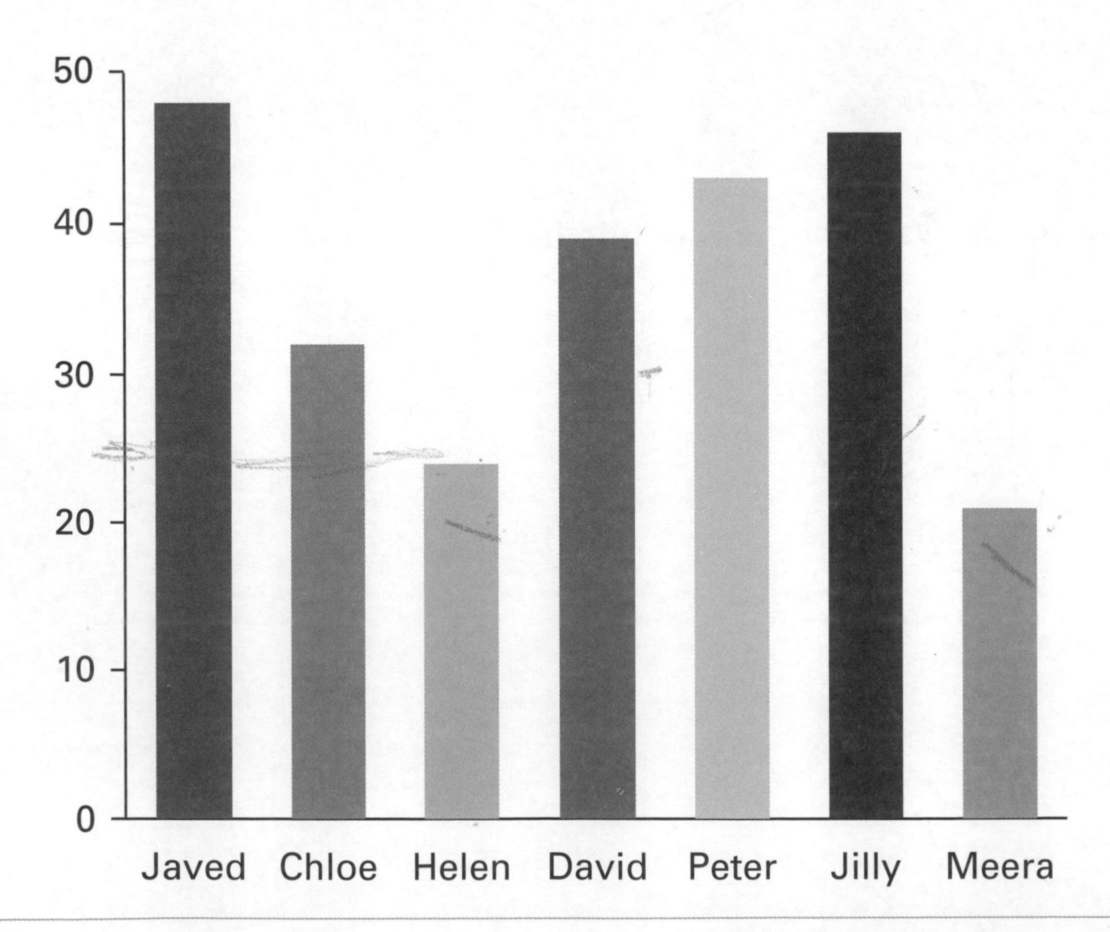

a) Whose scores are incorrect on the bar chart?

_____________ and _____________ *(1 mark)* ☐ Q14a

b) Who scored half the number of marks Javed got?

_____________________________ *(1 mark)* ☐ Q14b

c) How many **incorrect** spellings did David have? ☐ *(1 mark)* ☐ Q14c

15 Estimate the number marked by the arrow.

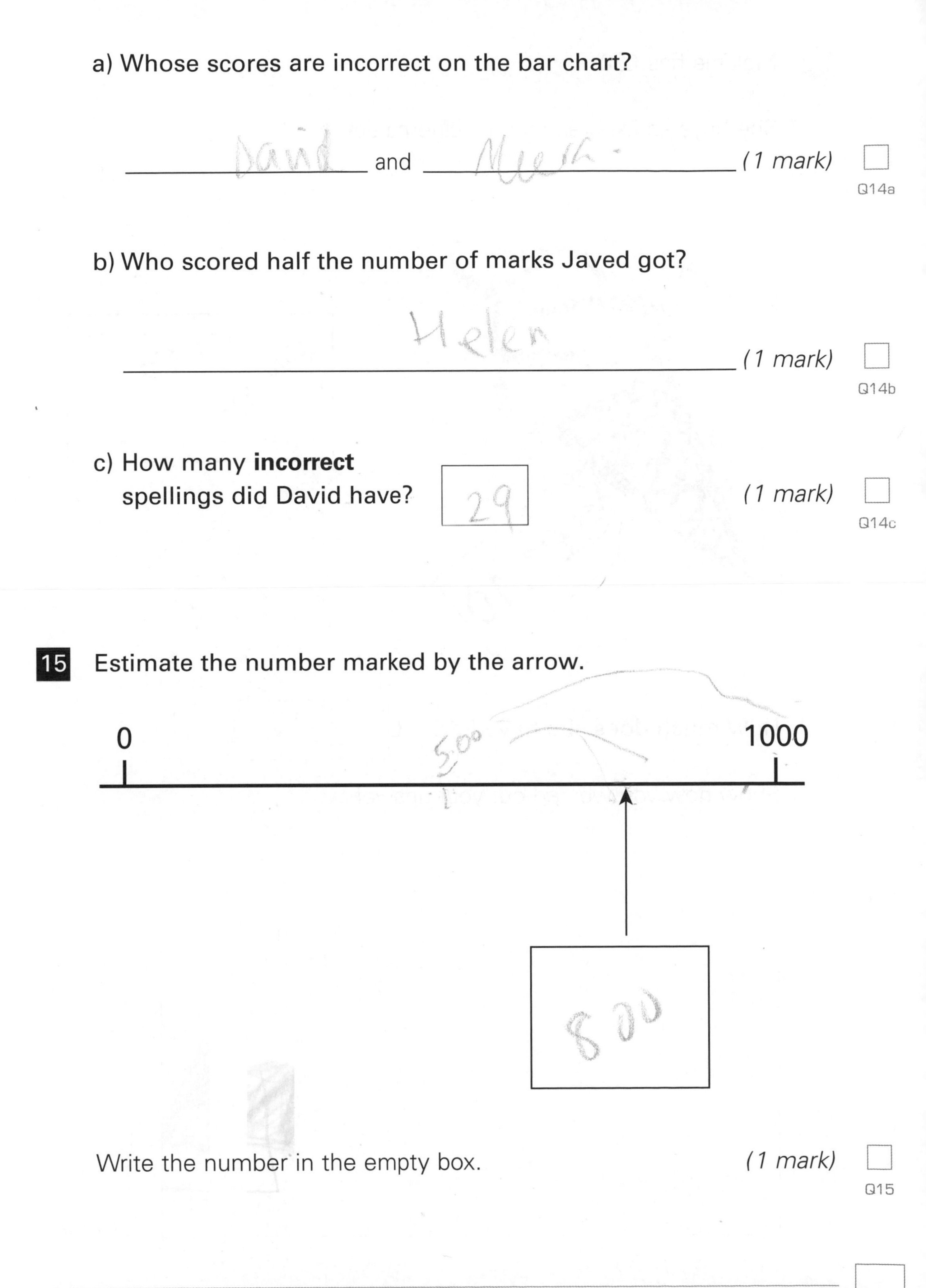

Write the number in the empty box. *(1 mark)* ☐ Q15

subtotal

16 Melanie has £20.

She buys an ice-cream and a cinema ticket.

How much does she have left? £

Show how you worked out your answer.

(1 mark)

Q16

17 Fill in the correct number.

237 + ☐ = 658

(1 mark) ☐ Q17

18 Draw the reflection of this shape in the mirror line.

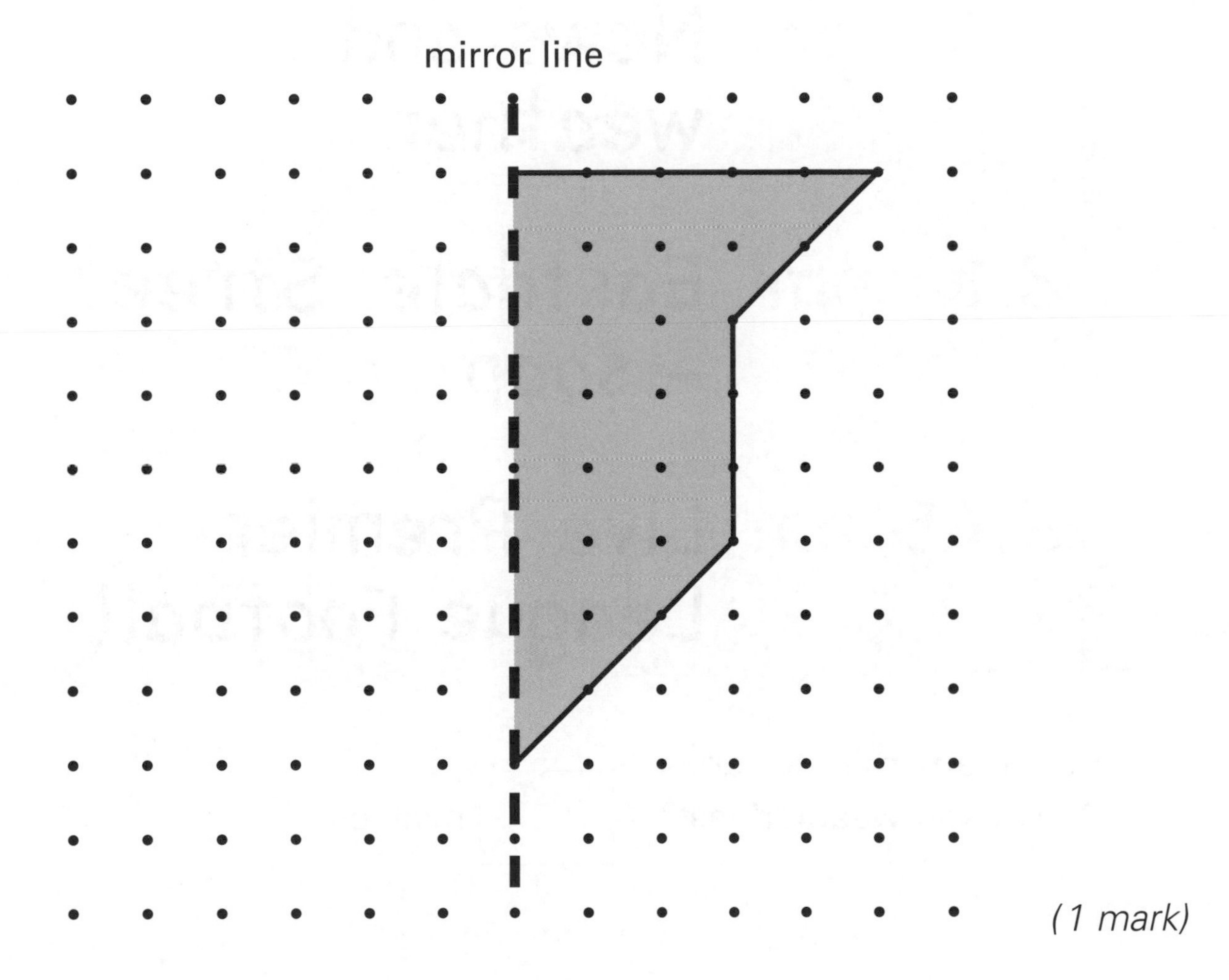

(1 mark) ☐ Q18

subtotal

19

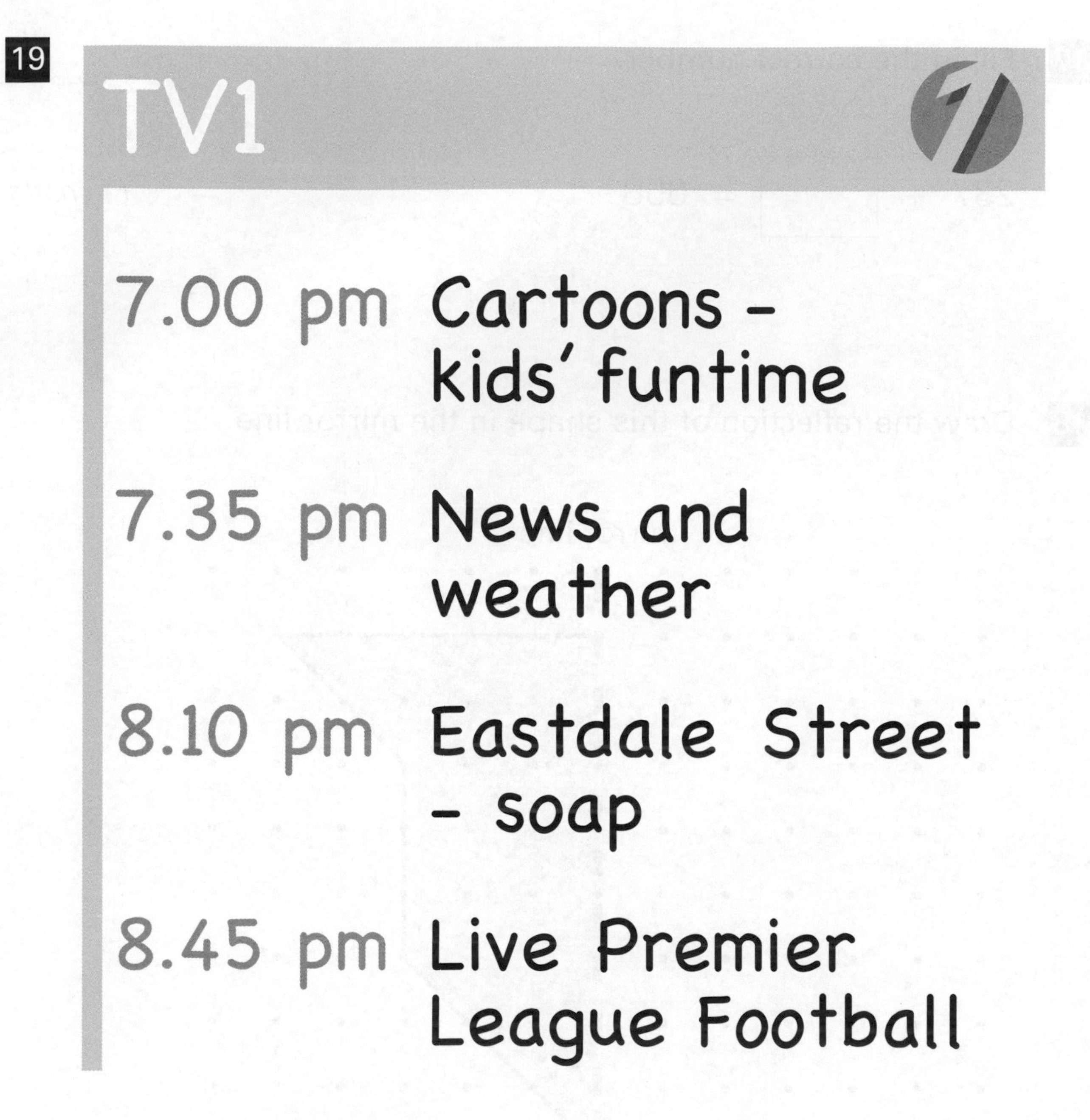

How many minutes does 'News and weather' last? ☐ minutes *(1 mark)*

Q19

20 In his shopping bag, Tariq has 2 kg of potatoes, 500 g of carrots and $1\frac{1}{2}$ kg of onions.

What does his shopping bag weigh? ☐ kg *(1 mark)*

Q20

subtotal

21

	has 3 digits	does not have 3 digits
odd	173	61
even		1004

Write these numbers in the correct place on the chart.

7939 240 637 *(1 mark)*

Q21

22 **Write a number in each box to make this correct.**

$600 \div 3 = \square \times \square$ *(1 mark)*

Q22

23 **Write the answer.**

$500 - 37 = \square$ *(1 mark)*

Q23

24 Saul has a bottle of fruit smoothie.

Tick (✔) the capacity the bottle is most likely to be.

☐ 20 ml

☐ 200 ml

☐ 1500 ml

☐ 3 litres

☐ 5 litres

(1 mark) ☐ Q24

 subtotal

25 Carl worked out the correct answer to **84 ÷ 6**.

His answer was **14**.

Show how he could have worked out his answer.

(1 mark)

Q25

26 Amrita is thinking of a number.

What number is she thinking of? ☐ *(1 mark)*

☐ Q26

 subtotal

27 **Match each addition to its answer.**

One has been done for you.

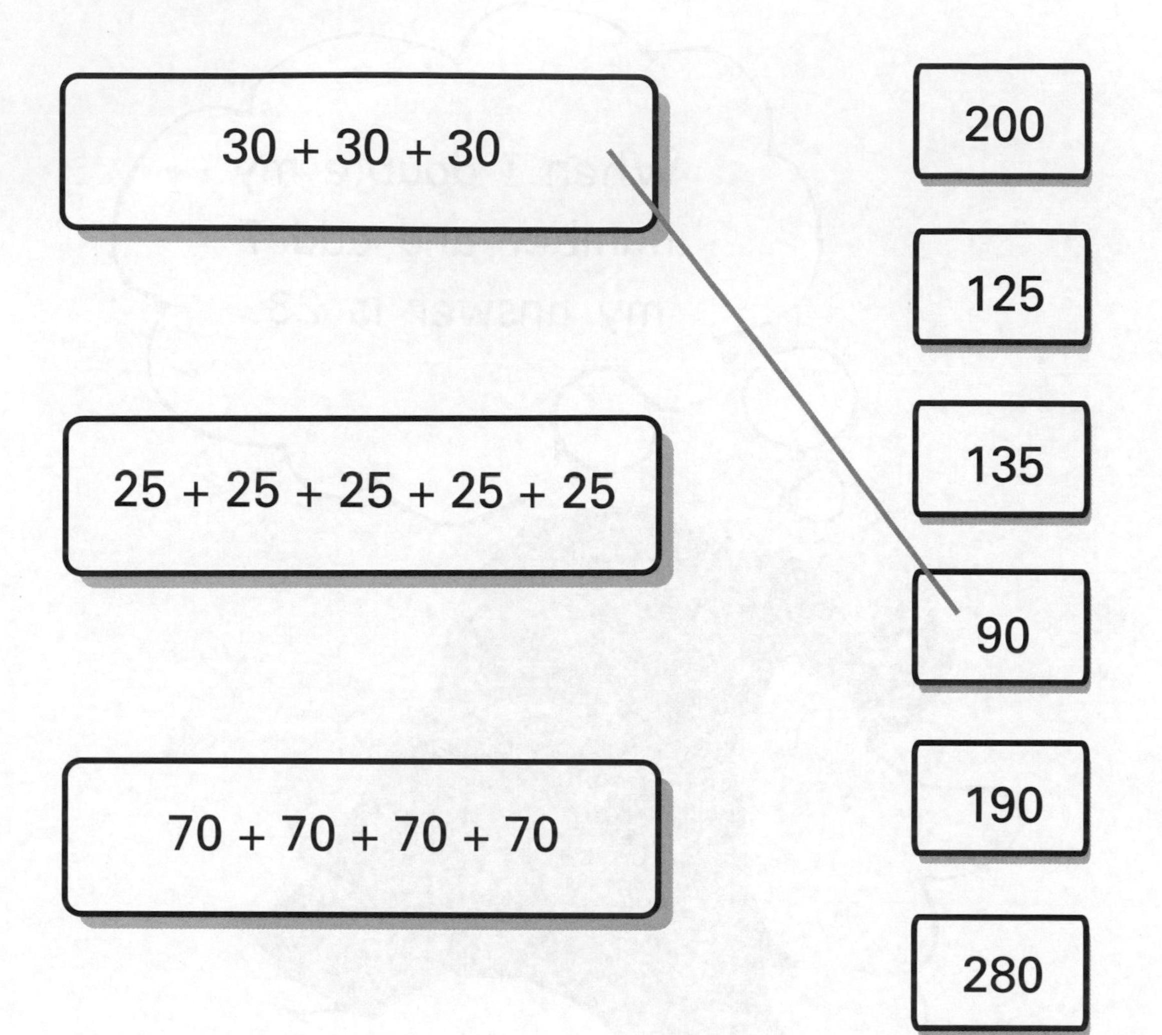

(1 mark)

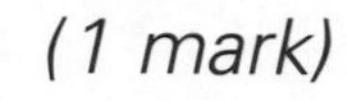

Q27

END OF TEST

subtota

KEY STAGE 1
Level 3
Test Paper C

Maths

Test Paper C

Instructions:

- find a quiet place where you can sit down and complete the test paper undisturbed
- an adult will need to read the first 5 questions to you
- make sure you have all the necessary equipment to complete the test paper (a pencil, rubber, ruler and small mirror)
- read the questions carefully
- answer all the questions in this paper
- go through and check your answers when you have finished the test paper

Time:

Take as long as necessary to complete the test paper but aim to complete it within 1 hour. Take a break halfway through.

Note to Parents:

Check how your child has done using pages 69–70 of the Answers and Mark Scheme.

Test Paper C

Test Paper C

Page	45	47	49	51	53	55	57	59	61	Max. Mark	**Actual Mark**
Score	....	....	....	....	....	....	....	....	....	30	....

First name ....

Last name ....

Read out these questions carefully to your child. Explain that they should listen to you and then write the answers on the opposite page.

What is the total of 12, 9 and 6? **Write your answer in box a.**

2 A film starts at 6:30pm and finishes at 8:00pm.
How long does the film last? **Write your answer in box b.**

3 What is the difference between 65 and 42? **Write your answer in box c.**

4 Asif bought 3 packs of stickers at 15p each.
How much change did he get from 50p? **Write your answer in box d.**

5 Look at the shapes. **Circle the 2 shapes that have 4 right angles.**

Now continue with the rest of the paper on your own.

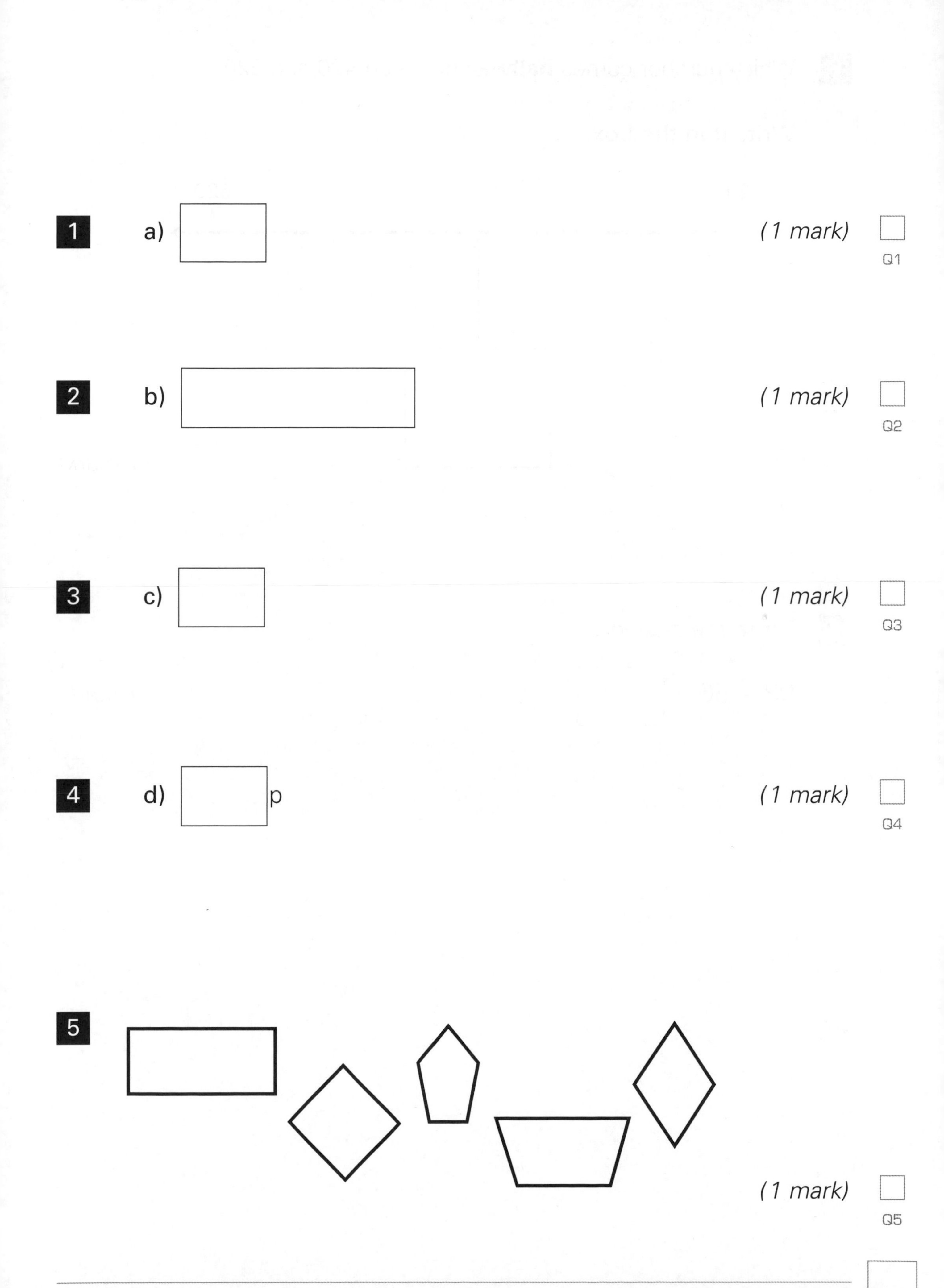

1 a) (1 mark) Q1

2 b) (1 mark) Q2

3 c) (1 mark) Q3

4 d) p (1 mark) Q4

5 (1 mark) Q5

subtotal

6 Which number comes **halfway** between 420 and 520?

Write it in the box.

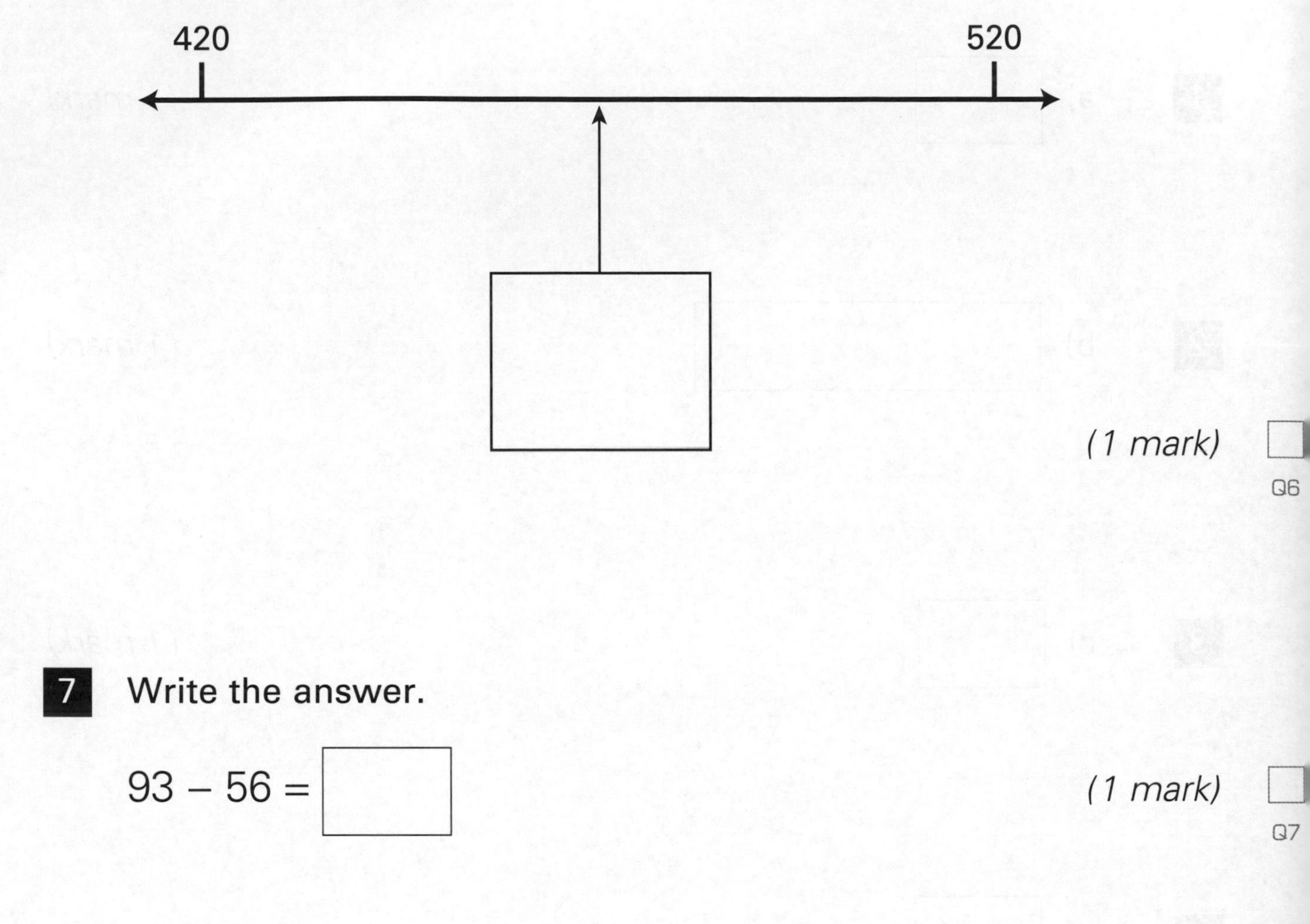

(1 mark)

Q6

7 **Write the answer.**

93 – 56 = ☐

(1 mark)

Q7

8 Draw lines to show where you would fold this shape to make a cube.

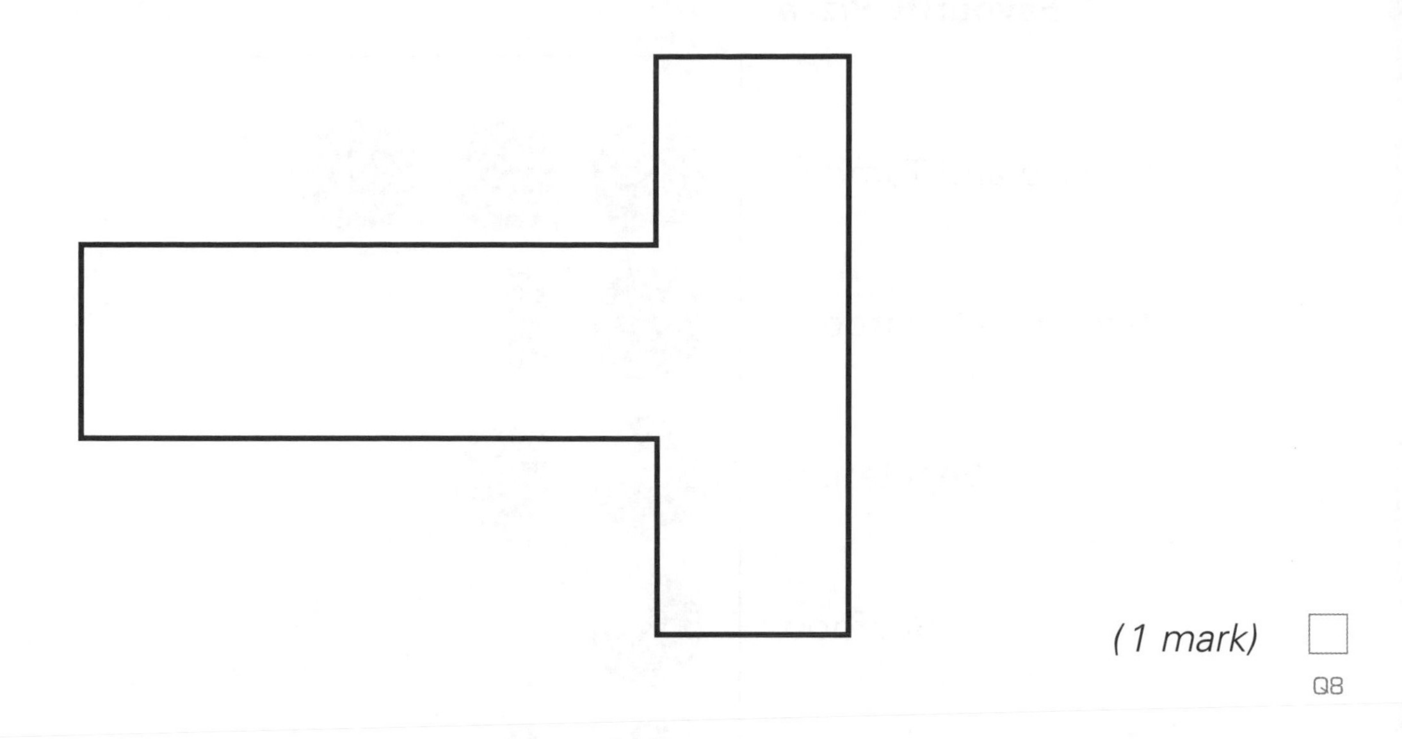

(1 mark)

Q8

9 Draw an arrow to show 750 g on the scale.

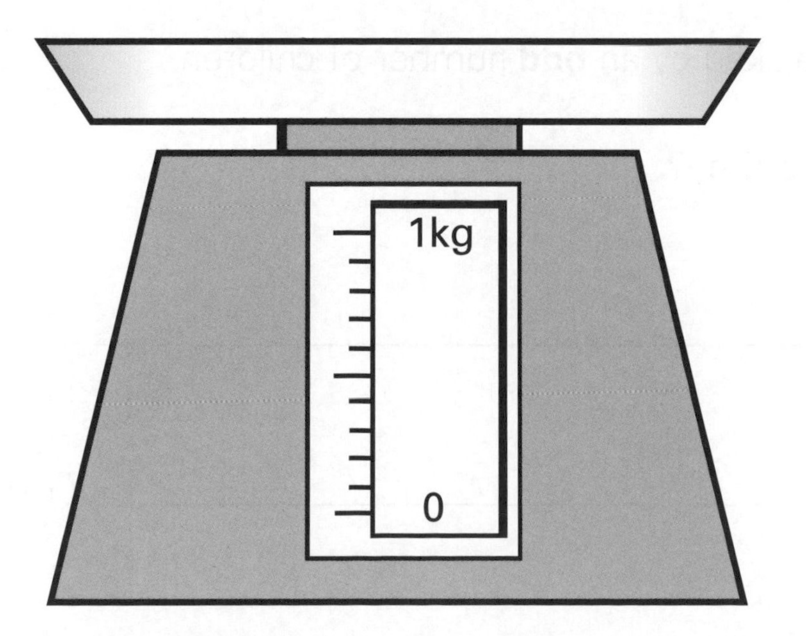

(1 mark)

Q9

subtotal

10 Look at the pictogram.

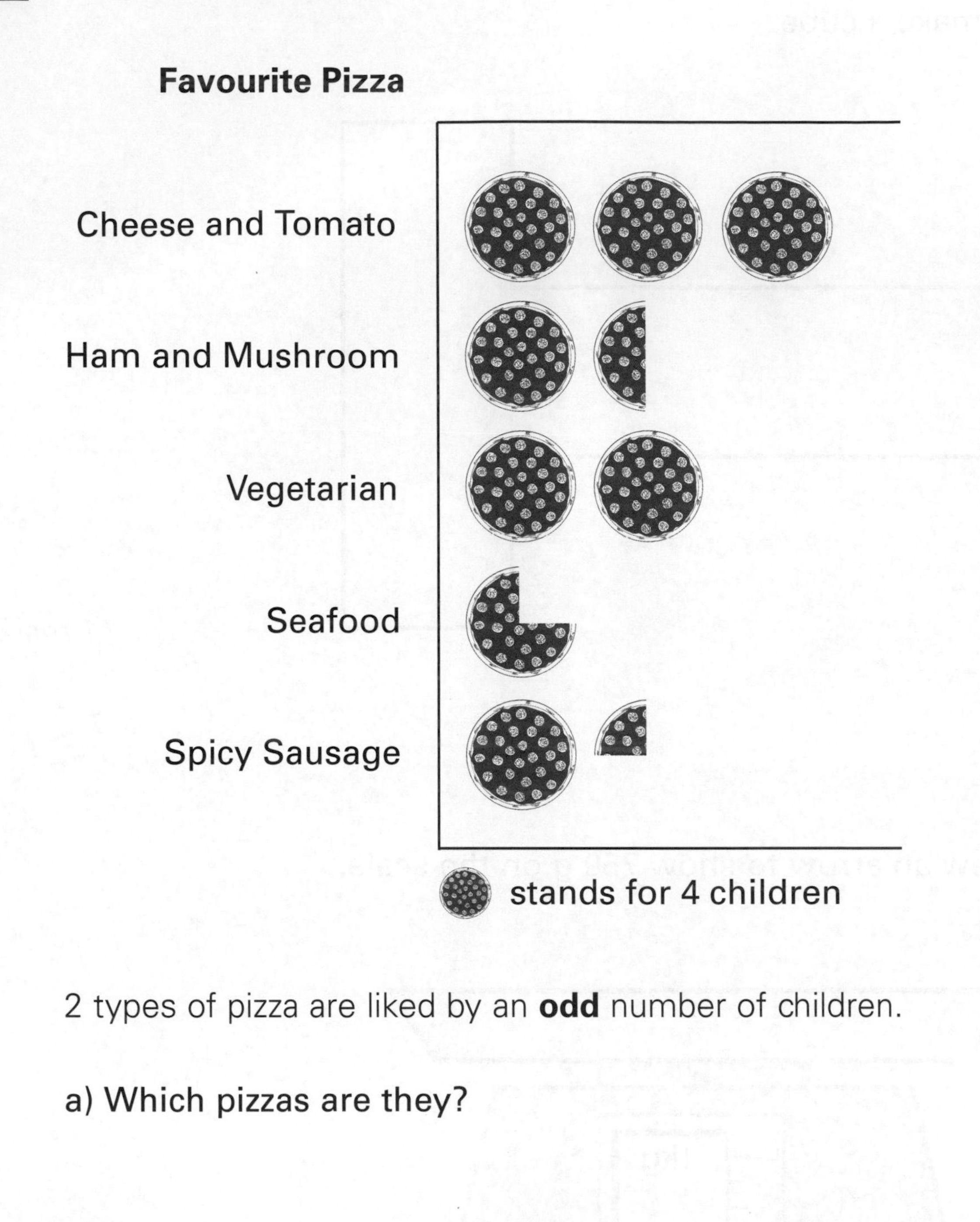

2 types of pizza are liked by an **odd** number of children.

a) Which pizzas are they?

____

and ______________________________ *(1 mark)*

Q10a

b) How many children took part in this survey? ☐ children *(1 mark)*

Q10b

11 **Write these numbers in the circles.**

All the numbers must be in order.

308 398 393

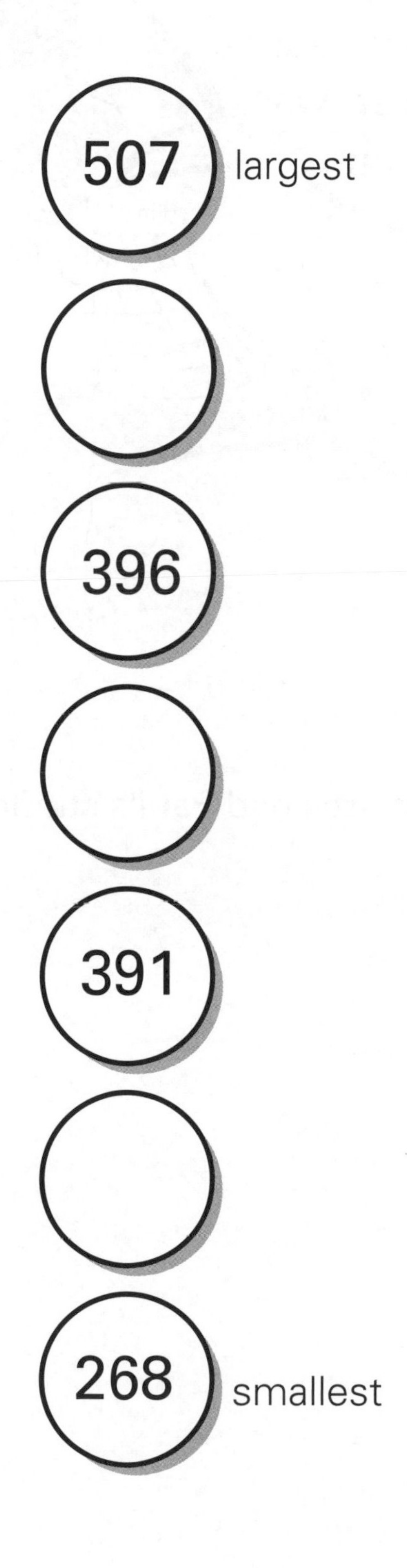

(1 mark)

Q11

subtotal

12

How many centimetres had Paul's sunflower grown?

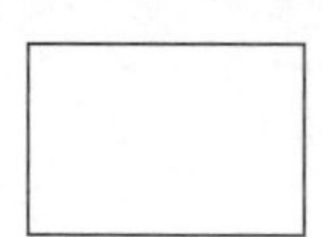 centimetres *(1 mark)*

Q12

13 Draw 2 **lines of symmetry** on this shape. You may use a mirror.

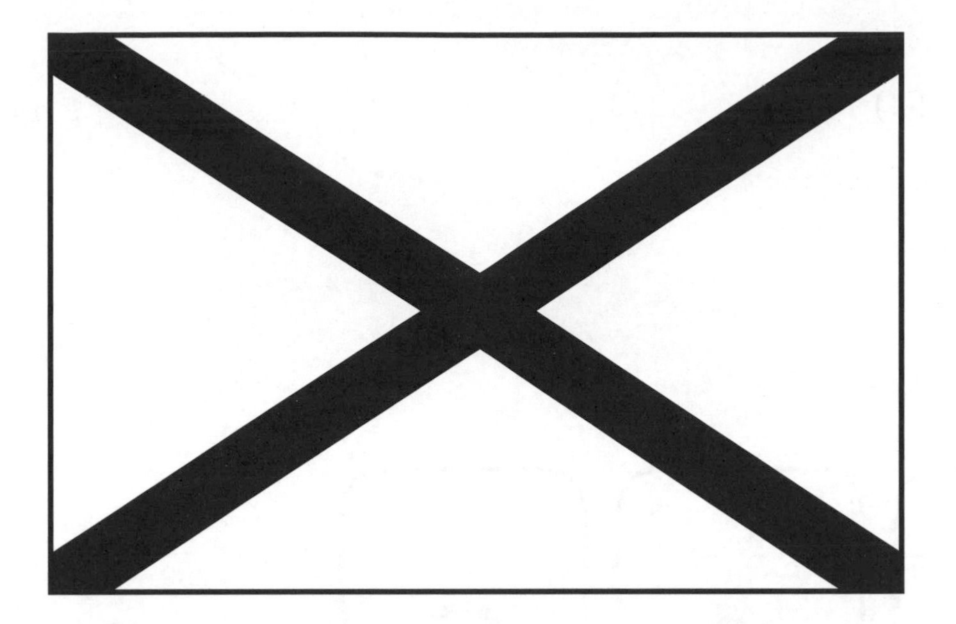

(1 mark) Q13

14 Sally is making a set of 4 wooden shelves. Each shelf is 80 cm long.

What length of wood does she need to buy? *(1 mark)* Q14

subtotal

Write the answer.

☐ = 90 ÷ 5

(1 mark)

Q15

16 Look at the digit cards.

Use all the digits to make the number nearest to 900.

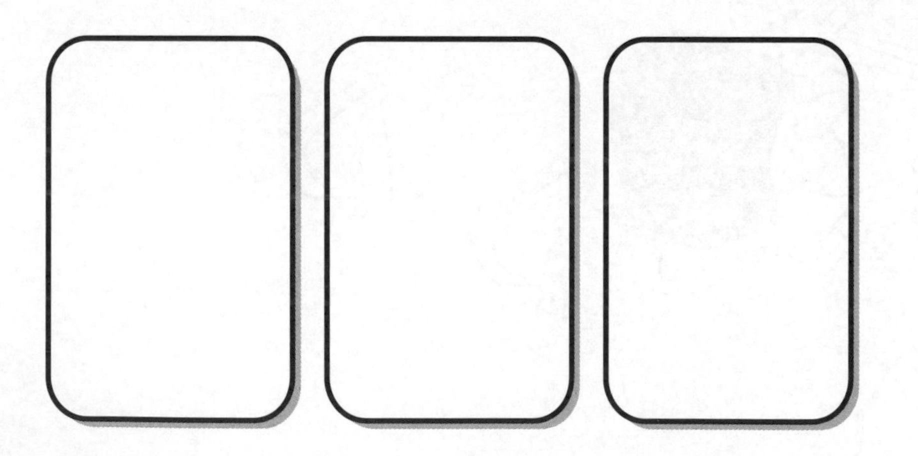

(1 mark)

Q16

17 Circle the 2 numbers which total 70.

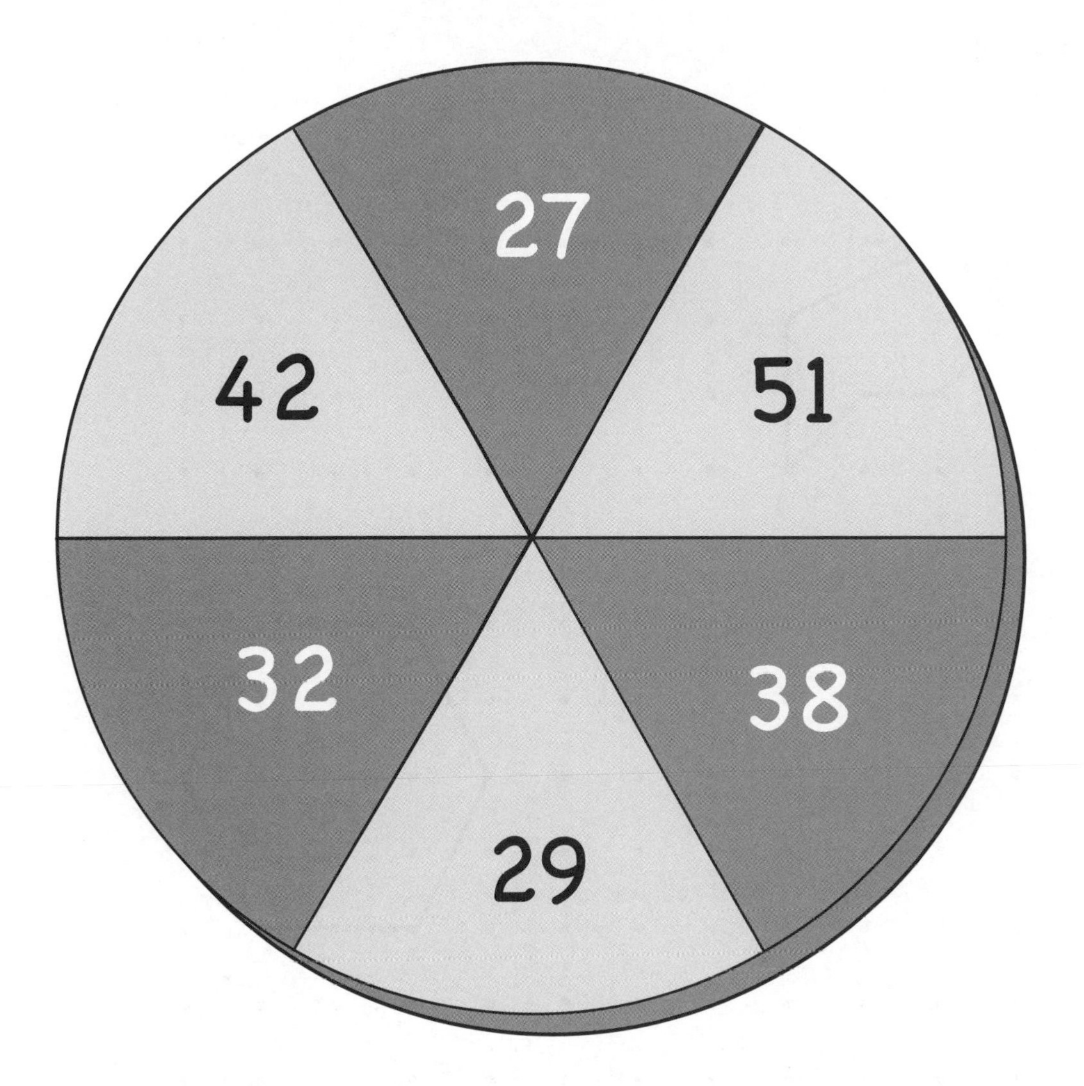

(1 mark)

Q17

subtotal

18 Use the dots to draw a **different** hexagon.

Use a ruler.

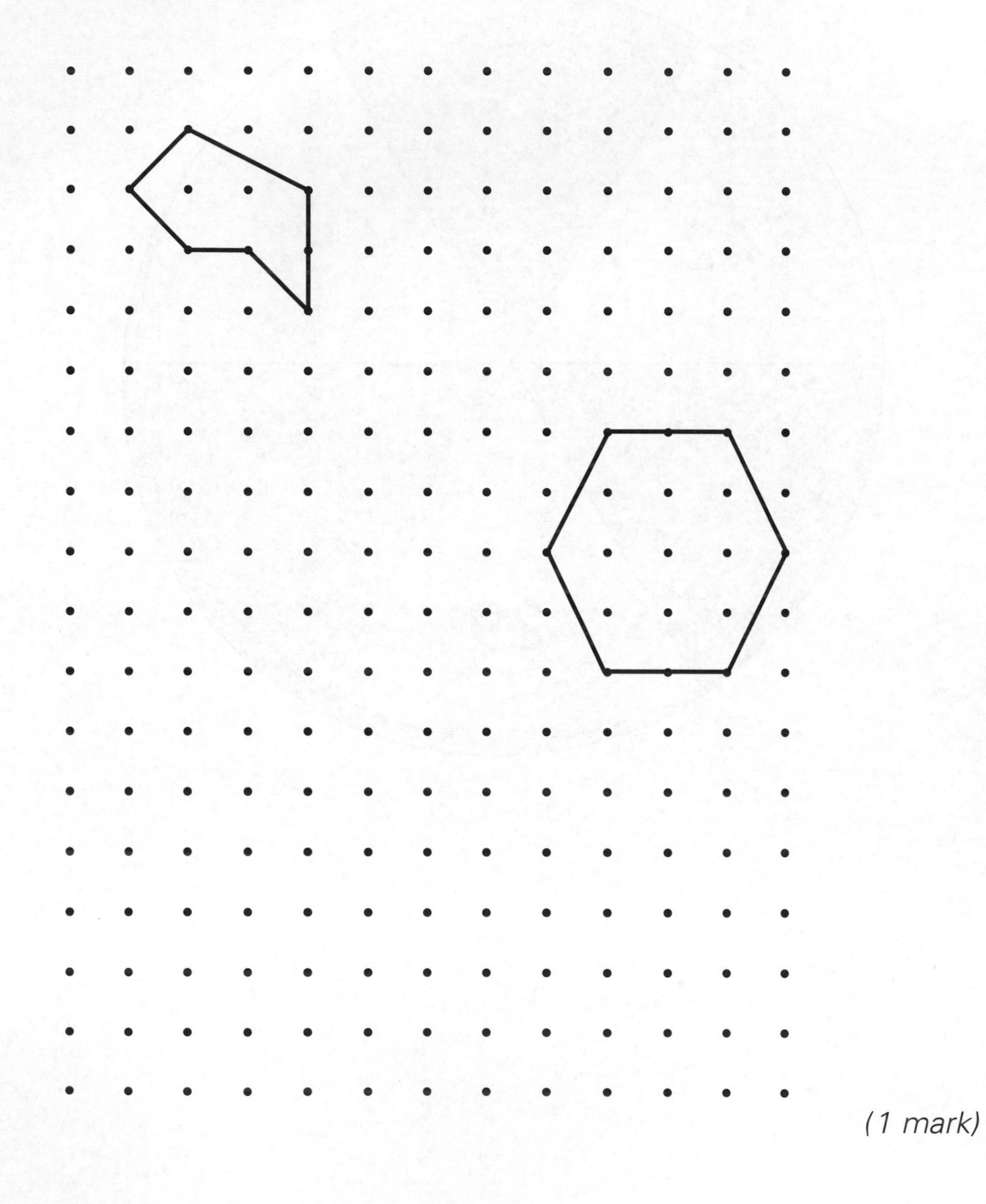

(1 mark) Q18

19 Look at the bar chart.

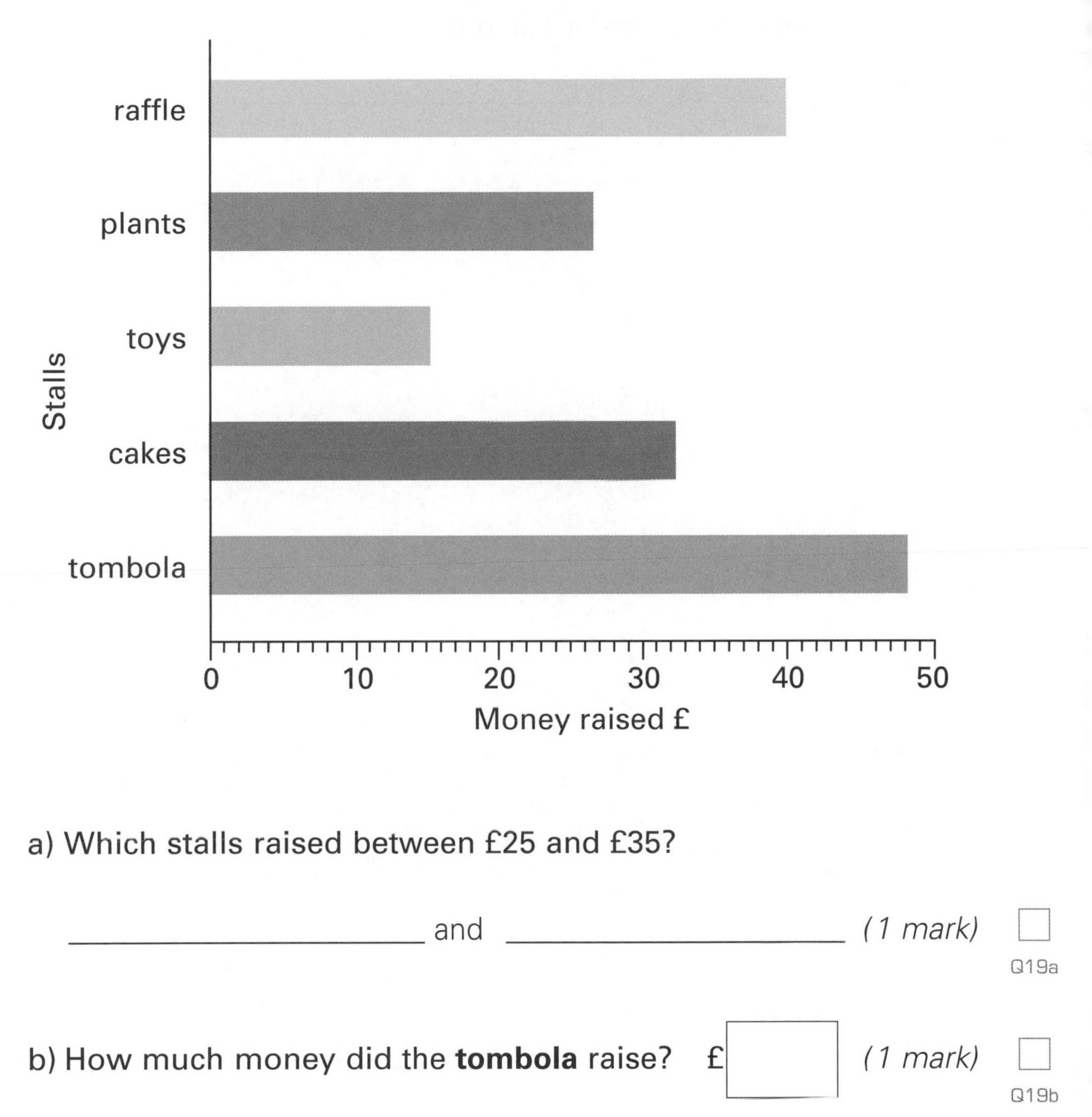

a) Which stalls raised between £25 and £35?

_________________________ and _________________________ *(1 mark)* Q19a

b) How much money did the **tombola** raise? £ [ ] *(1 mark)* Q19b

subtotal

20 **Add together 34, 57 and 35.**

Show how you worked it out in the box.

(1 mark)

Q20

21 Jo saved £5 each week for 9 weeks.

She wants to buy an MP3 player for £80.

How much more money does she need to save? £ [ ]

(1 mark)

Q21

subtotal

22 Marvin needs 20 burgers for his barbecue.

Burgers come in packs of 6.

a) How many packs does he need to buy? ☐ packs *(1 mark)* ☐

Q22a

His barbecue starts at 7:15 and lasts for $1\frac{1}{2}$ hours.

b) Circle the time it finishes.

7:45 9:00 8:15

8:45 9:30

(1 mark) ☐

Q22b

23 Look at this sequence.

224 112 56 28 14 7

Tick (✔) the rule for this sequence.

☐ divide by 3

☐ add 7

☐ subtract 10

☐ divide by 2

(1 mark) ☐ Q23

24 **Put a ring around the 2 numbers which divide by 5 with no remainder.**

(1 mark) ☐ Q24

25 Philip works out the answer to **379 + 453**.

His answer is **382**.

Philip's answer is **wrong**.

Show how to work out the correct answer.

(1 mark)

Q25

26 Write the answer.

$60 \times 5 =$ ☐

(1 mark) ☐ Q26

27 Write the correct number in the box.

1067 —— to the nearest 100 ——→ ☐

(1 mark) ☐ Q27

END OF TEST

subtotal

Notes

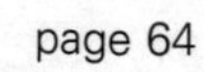

Answers and Mark Scheme

Maths Test Paper A

1) 8 *(1 mark)*
Note to parent – *This question aims to encourage your child to subtract mentally while recognising that the wording 'less than' suggests a subtraction operation.*

2) 20 children *(1 mark)*
Note to parent – *Your child needs to be able to count in 5s or recall facts from the x5 table. This question puts the multiplication operation in a real-life context.*

3) *(1 mark)*
Note to parent – *An understanding of the properties of 2D shapes is needed. Your child should be aware that triangles have 3 sides and there are lots of different types of triangle. You could look for different triangles in the environment – e.g. road signs, paving patterns, etc.*

4) $20 \div 5$ *(1 mark)*
Note to parent – *This question encourages your child to work out each of the 4 operations of addition, subtraction, multiplication and division. Division facts are related to multiplication facts and your child should know that $20 \div 5$ can be derived from 4×5.*

5) *(1 mark)*

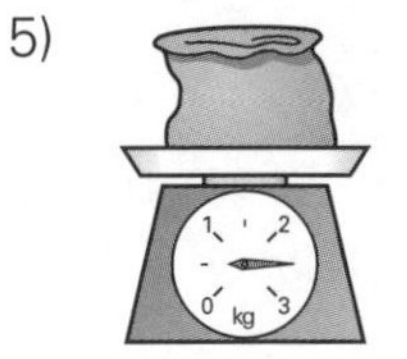

Note to parent – *Children should be able to read simple scales on rulers, weighing scales, clocks and capacity measures. The most effective way for children to learn to read scales is through practical activities – e.g. cooking, craft activities and telling the time.*

6) 14 stickers *(1 mark)*
Note to parent – *Your child should be able to recall number bonds (numbers which add up or subtract) to 20. They may also use visual clues to add on, starting with the largest number.*

7) ✔ *(1 mark)*
Note to parent – *Encourage your child to use language associated with shape and the names of shapes – e.g. long, short, corner, hexagon, right angle, etc. Look for shapes in the environment and encourage pattern-making as an art activity.*

8) a) and b)
Any 2 pairs of numbers that total 19 – e.g. 10 + 9, 2 + 17, etc. All 4 numbers must be different to achieve both marks. 1 mark may be awarded if both answers given are the same. *(2 marks)*
Note to parent – *As mentioned in question 6, your child needs to be secure with number bonds to 20. You can play games such as number ping-pong with a starting number – e.g. 15. You each take turns to say the numbers which add up – e.g. 8 & 7, 9 & 6.*

9) 8p *(1 mark)*
Note to parent – *Encourage your child to become familiar with real coins, making totals and finding change. This question involves adding on from 15 to get to 23 and an understanding of 'how much more'.*

10) 22 *(1 mark)*
Note to parent – *Your child should look for pairs of numbers that make 10. Then add on from the largest number.*

11) 23 = 47 – 24 or 23 = 67 – 44, or any other numbers where the first is greater than the second by 2. *(1 mark)*
Note to parent – *The first missing digit must be greater by 2 than the second missing digit. Your child should use their knowledge of place value in recognising that the tens digits need to have a difference of 2.*

12) 47 satsumas *(1 mark)*
Note to parent – *Counting in tens is a very useful and efficient activity in problem solving. It helps with children's understanding of place value and the number system.*

13) 54, 49, 44, **39**, 34, 29, **24** *(1 mark)*
Note to parent – *Your child should recognise that the units digits are alternating between 4 and 9, and the sequence is counting back through the tens numbers. There are limitless numbers of sequences that can be made to practise this type of activity.*

14) The line should be 14 cm long. *(1 mark)*
Note to parent – *It is important that your child can accurately use a ruler marked in centimetres. Ensure they start measuring and drawing from zero. Children can do measuring around the home with rulers, tape measures and string. They should be able to begin to estimate lengths and order the size of objects.*

15) 4 and 12 or 17 and 9 *(1 mark)*
Note to parent – *This question requires an understanding of the term 'difference' between 2 numbers. Your child also needs to be able to count on from the smaller number or back from the larger number.*

16) 40, 10, 90
(all 3 numbers must be circled) *(1 mark)*
Note to parent – *Your child should be able to recognise numbers divisible by 10 as those which have a zero as the units digit.*

17) 3 children *(1 mark)*
Note to parent – *Pictograms are a common way of displaying information in a visual way. Your child can carry out surveys at home about favourite pets, fruit, TV programmes, etc. and display the information as a pictogram.*

18) 103 *(1 mark)*
Note to parent – *Your child should have an understanding of the value of each digit in 3-digit numbers. They could make cards with individual digits on them, then make hundreds numbers and order them. They could also collect 3-digit numbers from car registration plates and order them.*

19) *(1 mark)*
Note to parent – *Your child should know that a rectangle has 2 pairs of equal sides. A square is also a rectangle where both pairs of sides are equal.*

20) a) 7 marbles *(1 mark)*
b) 2p *(1 mark)*
Note to parent – *Your child should be able to count in 5s and recall facts in the ×5 table. This question also involves calculating the remainder from a division problem involving money.*

21) 12 *(1 mark)*
Note to parent – *Your child should be able to add 8 on from 13. They may recognise that 9 is 1 more than 8 so the other number has to be 1 less than 13.*

22) 18 *(1 mark)*
Note to parent – *Knowing doubles of numbers up to 20 is useful in addition problems.*

23) a) 1, 5, 9, **13**, 17, **21**, 25 *(1 mark)*
b) 26, 22, **18**, **14**, 10, **6**, 2 *(1 mark)*
All the numbers are needed for each mark.
Note to parent – *Encourage your child to look at all the numbers in the sequences to establish a pattern. Both patterns involve differences of 4.*

24) *(1 mark)*

Note to parent – *Encourage your child to read both analogue (dial) and digital clocks and associate times with events – e.g. start and end of school, favourite TV programme, bedtime, etc. Ensure the minute hand is longer than the hour hand when drawing on analogue clocks.*

25) 38 *(1 mark)*
Note to parent – *Your child should recognise the language 'less than' as subtraction. They may count back 10 first, then the 2. A number line is useful for visualising counting back.*

26) 17 people *(1 mark)*
Note to parent – *This is a real-life problem requiring the operation of subtraction. Encourage your child to solve real-life problems involving all 4 operations of number.*

27) *(1 mark)*

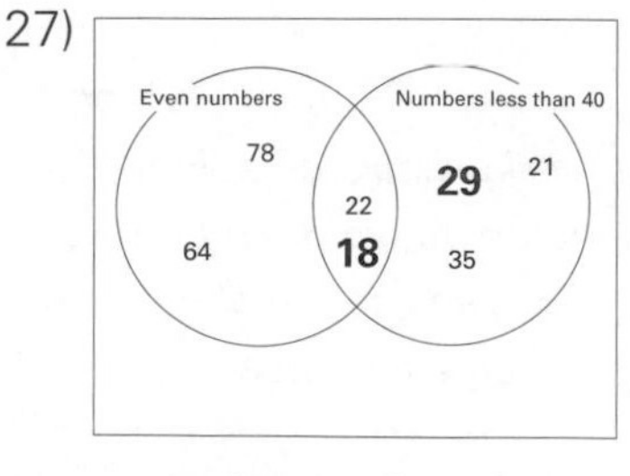

Note to parent – *Venn diagrams are a way of representing information with 2 or more variables. This question also requires an understanding of odd and even numbers.*

Maths Test Paper B

1) £41 *(1 mark)*
Note to parent *– Your child will have developed mental strategies for adding two 2-digit numbers. They may start with the larger number, then partition the other number into tens and units, then add each in turn – i.e. $23 + 10 = 33$, $33 + 8 = 41$.*

2) 90 & 2, 6 & 30, 1 & 180, etc. *(1 mark)*
Any 2 numbers that multiply together to make 180.
Note to parent *– Your child may use known facts – e.g. $9 \times 2 = 18$, so $90 \times 2 = 180$. As a practice activity you could give your child a number and ask them to find as many ways of making it using all 4 operations.*

3) 2 faces *(1 mark)*
Note to parent *– It is important that your child can visualise 3D shapes. They should be aware of how many faces regular solid shapes have.*

4) 1094 *(1 mark)*
Note to parent *– At Level 3, your child should be able to recognise the vocabulary of the number system and write corresponding numbers with 4 digits. They should understand the value of each digit in a number and in this number know that a zero is needed as the hundreds digit.*

5) kilograms *(1 mark)*
Note to parent *– Your child should have experience of the different units used to measure length, capacity, mass (weight) and time. Ensure they have plenty of practical experience around the home and when playing.*

6) $140 = 2 \times 70$ *(1 mark)*
Note to parent *– In this equation the answer is shown first. Your child should be familiar with this layout as well as the more conventional equation where the answer comes at the end.*

7) 30 5p pieces *(1 mark)*
Note to parent *– Your child may count in 5s up to 150 or recognise that there are three 5s in 15 so there must be thirty 5s in 150. Basic multiplication facts are very useful for solving a range of problems.*

8) £60.06, £6.60, £6.06, 66p, £0.60 *(1 mark)*
Note to parent *– All values must be in the correct order to achieve the mark. This question requires an understanding of place value and decimal notation for money. Playing shops at home is a fun way for children to learn the value of coins, find totals and work out change.*

9) *(1 mark)*

Note to parent *– Show your child that each mark is 100 ml and 50 ml is halfway between two. Practical experience when cooking is the best way for your child to learn about weighing and measuring.*

10) *(1 mark)*

■	■	
	■	

Note to parent *– Your child may find it easier to rotate the page to see how the pattern changes with each $\frac{1}{4}$ turn. They can learn about $\frac{1}{2}$ and $\frac{1}{4}$ turns by making maps, following directions, etc. when playing.*

11) 190 *(1 mark)*
Note to parent *– Encourage your child to see pairs of numbers that can be added easily, e.g. $6 + 4$, and start with the bigger number: $116 + 4 = 120$, $120 + 70 = 190$.*

12) a) 765 *(1 mark)*
b) 576 *(1 mark)*
Note to parent *– Again, your child needs to understand the value of each digit in a 3-digit number. They also need to know that an even number must end in 0, 2, 4, 6 or 8.*

13) 75 ml *(1 mark)*
Note to parent *– Your child should be able to work out a $\frac{1}{4}$ of an amount by halving and halving again. At Level 3, they need to be able to solve word problems, identifying what operation is needed.*

14) a) Meera and David *(1 mark)*
b) Helen *(1 mark)*
c) 29 *(1 mark)*
Note to parent *– At Level 3, children need to extract and interpret information displayed in bar charts, lists and tables. This is a vertical bar chart. Bar charts may also be orientated horizontally.*

15) Any number between 750 and 850 *(1 mark)*
Note to parent *– Using unmarked number lines enables your child to gain a better understanding of the number system, while estimating and approximating numbers up to 1000.*

16) £16.20 *(1 mark)*
Note to parent *– This is a multi-step problem which requires your child to add the value of the ice-cream and cinema ticket, then subtract this amount from £20. Encourage them to write each step of the solution.*

17) 421 *(1 mark)*
Note to parent *– When your child is faced with an equation with a missing number, they will need to use their understanding of inverse operations. In this question, they may count on from 237 to 658 on a number line or subtract 237 from 658.*

18) *(1 mark)*
Note to parent *– Use a mirror to help your child see where the mirror line or line of symmetry is. Look for other symmetrical shapes around the home.*

19) 35 minutes *(1 mark)*
Note to parent *– Ensure your child understands how to read times, calculate periods of time and solve problems. TV guides and timetables are very useful everyday ways of practising these skills.*

20) 4 kg *(1 mark)*
Do not accept '$3\frac{1}{2}$ kg and 500 g'.
Note to parent *– Your child needs to recognise that 500 g is equivalent to $\frac{1}{2}$ kg. Take items from the kitchen and ask them to add the total weight. Weigh loose fruits and vegetables in the supermarket on the scales.*

21) *(1 mark)*

	has 3 digits	does not have 3 digits
odd	173 **637**	61 **7939**
even	**240**	1004

Note to parent *– All 3 numbers must be in the correct boxes to gain the mark. Carroll diagrams are a way of representing information with 2 variables.*

22) 20 & 10, 200 & 1, 4 & 50, etc. *(1 mark)*
Any 2 numbers that multiply together to make 200.
Note to parent *– Your child needs to work out the division first, then identify 2 numbers to multiply together to make 200. They may use known facts – e.g. $2 \times 10 = 20$ so $20 \times 10 = 200$, $4 \times 5 = 20$ so $4 \times 50 = 200$.*

23) 463 *(1 mark)*
Note to parent *– Your child may round the 37 up to 40, then subtract to give $500 - 40 = 460$. Then they will need to add the 3 back on, so $460 + 3 = 463$. They may round 37 down to 30, so $500 - 30 = 470$, then subtract the further 7, $470 - 7 = 463$.*

24) 200 ml *(1 mark)*
Note to parent *– Your child needs to have an understanding of estimated quantities of measures – e.g. a door is about 2 m high, a newborn baby weighs about 3 kg, a film lasts about 2 hours, etc. Take household objects and guess the approximate measures.*

25) A complete and correct method must be recorded for the mark to be awarded. *(1 mark)*
Note to parent *– Your child may show counting in 6s – 6, 12, 18, 24, etc. They may make 84 marks and separate them into 6 groups of 14. They may do a repeated subtraction $84 - 6 = 78$, $78 - 6 = 72$, etc. or show the inverse operation of $6 \times 14 = 84$.*

26) 8 *(1 mark)*
Note to parent *– Your child needs to work backwards from the total: $23 - 7 = 16$, $16 \div 2 = 8$. Try to make up some of these puzzles when in the car or walking to school.*

27) *(1 mark)*

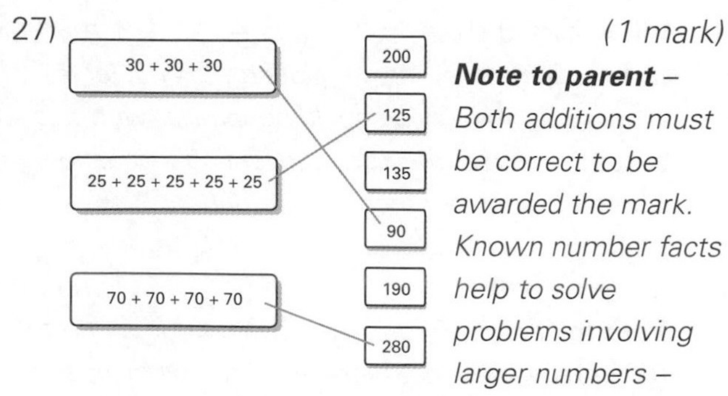

Note to parent *– Both additions must be correct to be awarded the mark. Known number facts help to solve problems involving larger numbers – e.g. $4 \times 7 = 28$ helps to solve 4×70.*

Maths Test Paper C

1) 27 *(1 mark)*
Note to parent *– Your child should be able to recall number bonds to 20 and add smaller numbers mentally.*

2) 1 hour 30 minutes or 90 minutes *(1 mark)*
Note to parent *– Using a film or TV guide sets challenges and problems for your child in real-life contexts so that they develop an understanding of time.*

3) 23 *(1 mark)*
Note to parent *– Your child should recognise the term 'difference' as subtraction. They may count on from the smaller number or subtract the tens and units separately.*

4) 5p *(1 mark)*
Note to parent *– This is a simple 2-step problem involving multiplication and subtraction. Encourage your child to use money in shops for buying small items so that they familiarise themselves with real-life money situations.*

5) *(1 mark)*
Note to parent *– Make a right-angle measurer from a corner of a piece of paper and encourage your child to look for right angles on shapes around the home.*

6) 470 *(1 mark)*
Note to parent *– In order to solve this problem, your child should find the difference between the 2 numbers, halve it, then add this on to the smaller number.*

7) 37 *(1 mark)*
Note to parent *– Your child will have developed a strategy for subtracting a 2-digit number while crossing the tens boundary. They may round 56 to 60, subtract this from 93, then add the extra 4 they subtracted. 93 – 60 = 33, 33 + 4 = 37. Encourage your child to check their answer by adding again, 56 + 37 = 93.*

8) 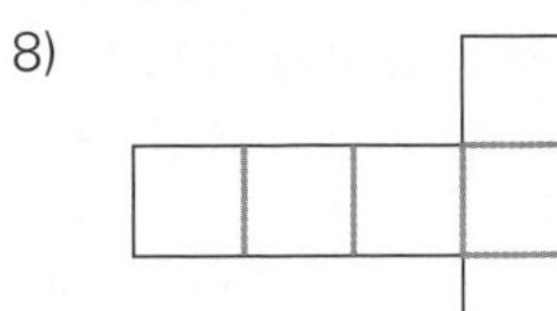 *(1 mark)*
Note to parent *– You can dismantle cereal packets, etc. to show the 'nets' of 3D shapes. It is important that your child can visualise 3D shapes from a 2D representation.*

9) 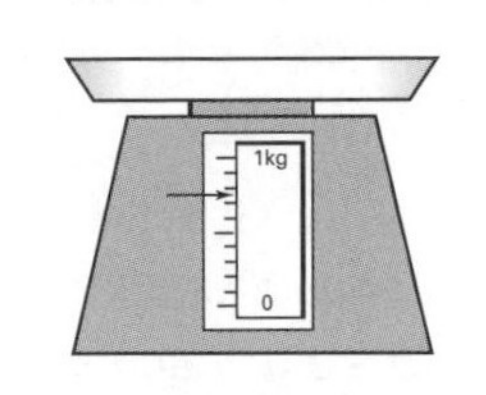

(1 mark)
Note to parent *– Scales can be represented vertically, horizontally or curved, as on bathroom scales. Ensure your child is familiar with a range of scales for measuring capacity and weight (mass).*

10) a) Seafood and Spicy sausage *(1 mark)*
b) 34 children *(1 mark)*
Note to parent *– Pictograms are a common way of representing information. Your child should identify that $\frac{3}{4}$ of the circle represents 3 children, $\frac{1}{2}$ of the circle represents 2 children and $\frac{1}{4}$ represents 1 child before they begin to answer the questions. Look out for pictograms in newspapers and magazines.*

11) 507, **398**, 396, **393**, 391, **308**, 268 *(1 mark)*
Note to parent *– Your child should have a secure understanding of place value of 3-digit numbers when working at Level 3.*

12) 58 centimetres *(1 mark)*
Note to parent *– This is a similar calculation to question 7, but puts subtraction in a practical, real-life context. Your child should use a similar strategy for solving it.*

13) 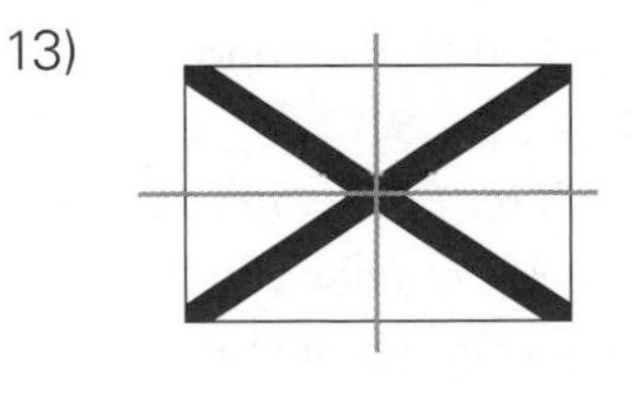 *(1 mark)*
Note to parent *– A mirror can be used to help locate where the lines of symmetry should be drawn.*

14) 320 cm or 3 m 20 cm *(1 mark)*
Note to parent *– Your child may do repeated addition of 80 + 80 + 80 + 80 or use 4 × 8 = 32, so 4 × 80 = 320. Encourage them to show the answer as metres and centimetres.*

15) 18 *(1 mark)*
Note to parent – *Your child may count in 5s up to 90, or know that there are twenty 5s in 100 so there must be 2 less in 90.*

16) 894 *(1 mark)*
Note to parent – *Your child may first be tempted to put 948 as the answer, but remind them to also work out the numbers before 900. This question tests their understanding of the place value of 3-digit numbers.*

17) 38 and 32 *(1 mark)*
Note to parent – *Your child should look for 2 units numbers which add up to 10 – e.g. 1 and 9, 2 and 8. Then they should look for the value of the tens numbers to make their final total.*

18) Any 6-sided shape that is different from those shown. All sides must join. Do not award the mark if an orientation of shape already shown is drawn. *(1 mark)*
Note to parent – *Vertices (corners) do not need to touch the dots to award the mark. Ensure your child knows the number of sides of these 2D shapes: circle, triangle, square, rectangle, pentagon, hexagon, octagon.*

19) a) plants and cakes *(1 mark)*
b) £48 (accept £47 or £49) *(1 mark)*
Note to parent – *This is a horizontal bar chart representing information. Your child needs to interpret the scale and estimate the values. They could carry out a survey at home about favourite fruits, TV programmes, etc. and make their own bar chart.*

20) 126 *(1 mark)*
Note to parent – *Your child will probably partition each number into tens and units, then add all the tens and all the units. 30 + 50 + 30 = 110, 4 + 7 + 5 = 16, 110 + 16 = 126. Encourage your child to play games where scores need to be added – e.g. darts, cards and board games.*

21) £35 *(1 mark)*
Note to parent – *This is a 2-step problem, first involving multiplication and then subtraction. Encourage your child to solve simple, real-life problems involving money when shopping and spending pocket money.*

22) a) 4 packs *(1 mark)*
Note to parent – *When solving real-life problems children need to understand the context and when to round up in division.*
b) 8:45 *(1 mark)*
Note to parent – *Encourage your child first to add on the hour, then the half hour, using an analogue clock to help understanding when adding times.*

23) divide by 2 *(1 mark)*
Note to parent – *Your child may also identify this as halving. Give your child a rule and a starting number for a sequence and see how far they can go.*

24) 35 and 70 *(1 mark)*
Both answers needed to get 1 mark
Note to parent – *Numbers exactly divisible by 5 are those which end in a 5 or 0.*

25) 832 *(1 mark)*
Note to parent – *Your child may use one of a number of strategies to solve this. They may add the hundred, the tens and the units separately, then total all three answers. They may use a number line or a formal column addition method if this has been taught.*

26) 300 *(1 mark)*
Note to parent – *Your child will need to calculate 60 × 5 using known number facts. They may recognise that 10 is double 5 so the missing number should be half of 600.*

27) 1100 *(1 mark)*
Note to parent – *This question requires an understanding of place value beyond 1000. When rounding to the nearest hundred, any number above and including 50 rounds up to the next hundred.*

Letts

KS1
Success

PRACTICE TEST PAPERS

Reading

Laura Griffiths

Contents

Introduction

Instructions on using the Practice Test Papers

Understanding Assessment

What is assessment?
Teacher assessment will form the main part of your child's result at the end of Key Stage 1 (at the age of 7). However, tests and tasks help to validate the teacher's own assessment.

What are the children tested on?
All children study the National Curriculum from Year 1. At the end of Year 2, the tests will assess your child's knowledge, skills and understanding in the programmes of study that they have followed from Year 1.

In English the programme of study covers three areas:
English 1: Speaking and Listening
English 2: Reading
English 3: Writing

What tests will my child take?
Teacher assessment for seven-year-olds covers:

- reading
- writing
- speaking and listening
- maths
- science

These assessments take account of how your child performed in Key Stage 1 tasks and tests. The tasks and tests cover:

- reading
- writing (including handwriting and spelling)
- maths

The tasks and tests are informal and can be taken at a time the school chooses, although they usually take place towards the end of Year 2. The tasks and tests last for less than three hours altogether and the results help to inform the teacher's overall assessment of your child. No statutory testing is carried out at Key Stage 1.

Can my child fail a test?
It is important that children understand they are not going to 'pass' or 'fail' the test – it will just show what they have learned and what they can do.

Preparing your Child for Tests

These practice test papers are designed to prepare your child for school tests by giving them the confidence of knowing the sort of questions they will experience.

These practice test papers will also help you to assess how your child is doing at school. They will give you an indication of your child's strengths and weaknesses, and how you can help them.

How can you improve your child's score?

- Mark the papers.
- Look at what your child got wrong and talk it through with them.
- Let your child do the test again.
- Remember, keep practising the things they get wrong. For example, if they find reading non-fiction difficult, give them plenty of practice.
- Try to encourage your child not to throw away marks, by reading a question carefully and checking their answer.

About these Practice Test Papers

In this book there are two sets of practice test papers for reading.

Each reading set contains:
Reading Test – Level 2 (a story, information and questions) *(30 marks)*
Reading Test – Level 3 (fiction reading material, non-fiction reading material and questions) *(25 marks)*

Taking the Tests

Set A and Set B are two different tests. First of all, give your child the Level 2 paper.

Remind them of the following:

- Read the questions carefully.
- Check your answers.

Your child cannot be given any help with reading words he or she does not know.

The test has to be all your child's own work.

When they have finished, mark the paper.

Look at the following tables to find out what they have achieved.

Marking the Tests and Assessing Levels

Write your child's scores into the grid below.

	Set A (Level 2)	Set B (Level 2)	Set A (Level 3)	Set B (Level 3)
Total				

Look at the table below to find out what your child has achieved in the Level 2 practice test papers. Level 2a is the highest.

Number of marks	Reading level
0–7	Level 2 not achieved
8–18	Level 2c
19–24	Level 2b
25–30	Level 2a

If your child achieves Level 2b or 2a, they should take the Level 3 paper.
Next mark your child's Level 3 paper and insert their score into the grid at the top of this page.
Now use the table below to determine your child's level of achievement.

Number of marks	Reading level
0–14	Level 3 not achieved. Your child has achieved Level 2
15+	Level 3 achieved

Please note: these tests are only a guide to the level your child can achieve and cannot guarantee the same level is achieved during school assessments.

How well has my child done in these tests?

The results show whether or not your child has reached the expected National Curriculum level at the age of 7.

Level	Aged 7
Level 1	Below average
Level 2 Level 2c Level 2b Level 2a	At level expected
Level 3	Excellent
Level 4	Exceptional
Level 5	
Level 6	
Level 7	
Level 8	

What do the levels mean?

When your child's reading paper is marked, the correct marks are collated to give your child an overall score. This score is then matched to a National Curriculum level. The government target for pupils at the end of Year 2 is to achieve Level 2. Some pupils will be working below this level and achieve Level 1, whilst other pupils will be working above the expected level and achieve Level 3.

KEY STAGE 1
Level 2

Reading
Test Paper

Level 2 Reading Test Paper

The Dog and the Bone & All About Dogs

Instructions:

- find a quiet place where you can sit down and complete the test paper undisturbed
- make sure you have all the necessary equipment to complete the test paper
- read the questions carefully
- answer the questions on the test paper
- go through and check your answers when you have finished writing

Time:

Take as long as necessary to complete the test paper but aim to complete it within 45 minutes.

Note to Parents:

Check how your child has done using pages 81–82 of the Answers and Mark Scheme.

Page	9	11	13	15	17	19	20	Max. Mark	**Actual Mark**
Score	....	....	....	....	....	....	....	30	....

First name ....

Last name ....

Reading

The Dog and the Bone & All About Dogs

The Dog and the Bone

Once upon a time there was an old dog that was greedy and very unkind. He was walking home one day when, all of a sudden, he came to a butcher's shop. The dog stopped and poked his nose through the door to get a closer smell of all those delicious meats. "Mmm," he thought. He loved the smell!

Practice Questions

A What type of dog was he? Circle the word.

clever greedy

kind brave

B Why did the dog stop outside the butcher's shop?

The Dog A Stopped outside the butchers to smell the meat/ Beaf or something.

After a while, the dog went into the butcher's shop and looked hungrily at all the different meats and tasty bones on the counter. There were lots of customers busy buying. The dog's tummy rumbled and he realised it was nearly dinner time. He began to feel extremely hungry.

1 What was the dog looking at on the counter? *(1 mark)*

Q1

The Dog was looking at the ~~[illegible]~~ differentmeat's and tasty bone

2 How did the dog feel? *(1 mark)*

Q2

He felt extremely hungry

subtotal

The dog could not help himself and when the butcher was not looking, he greedily snatched the biggest bone he could see.

The dog ran straight out of the shop and carried on running home with his new bone. He was very pleased with himself and he held the bone tightly between his teeth so he would not lose it.

3 What did the dog do when the butcher was not looking? Tick your answer. *(1 mark)* ☐ Q3

He snatched a bone. ☐

He licked a piece of meat. ☐

He barked loudly. ☐

He wagged his tail. ☐

4 Why did the dog hold the bone between his teeth? *(1 mark)* ☐ Q4

____

____

____

____

____

____

As the dog ran towards home, he came to a large stream. He was worried and did not know how to get across. Then, out of the corner of his eye, he noticed an old bridge.

The dog, still holding on tightly to his bone, decided to cross the bridge.

Half way over the bridge, the dog stopped and looked at his reflection in the water below him. All he could see was a dog holding a tasty, big bone. Being such a greedy, foolish dog, he wanted the bone the other dog was holding, so he growled and snapped at the dog in the water.

5 Write down two things that the dog saw as he was walking. *(2 marks)* Q5

a) ______________________________

b) ______________________________

6 Why did the dog growl at the water? *(1 mark)* Q6

____

____

____

____

subtotal

As he did this, he opened his mouth wide to show his sharp teeth, but immediately the bone fell from his mouth into the stream below him. The dog watched as the bone sank to the bottom. He could not reach it – it was lost forever.

"Oh no!" cried the dog. "My beautiful, tasty bone!" and he began to cry.

7 What did the dog do when the bone fell into the water? *(1 mark)* Q7

____

____

____

____

8 Why do you think the dog began to cry?
Tick your answer. *(1 mark)* Q8

He was lonely.	☐	He did not like water.	☐
He could not reach the bone.	☐	He was lost.	☐

9 Tick two words which describe the lost bone. *(2 marks)* Q9

beautiful	☐	juicy	☐
tasty	☐	big	☐

The dog was very sad and he wished that he had not tried to be greedy and have two bones, because now he was left with nothing.

Slowly and miserably, the hungry dog walked home, his tail down and his face covered in tears.

The dog learnt his lesson on that bridge and from that day on, he was never greedy again.

10 How do we know the dog was upset as he walked home? *(2 marks)*

Q10

____

____

____

____

11 What do you think the moral of the story is?
Tick your answer. *(1 mark)*

Q11

Be happy with what you have.	☐	Don't walk over a bridge.	☐
Never eat meat.	☐	Stay away from water.	☐

subtotal

All About Dogs

You have just read a story called "The Dog and the Bone", about a dog that was greedy and unkind.

In the next part of this test, you are going to read about dogs. There is some information about types of dogs and a guide on how to keep them as pets.

Practice Questions

A What will the next part of this test tell you about?
Circle your answer.

bones	dogs
fables	cats

B What are you going to read in the next part of this test?
Tick two things.

Information ☐	A story ☐	A recipe ☐
A guide ☐	A poem ☐	A letter ☐

Dogs are very clever animals and they can make excellent pets. There are many different breeds of dogs. The table below shows some of them.

Labradors	This is the most popular type of dog in the world today. Labradors can be one of three colours – yellow, black or chocolate.
Terriers	These are lively little dogs.
Chinese Crested	Some Chinese Crested are born with no hair.
Chihuahuas	These dogs come from Mexico. They are small and easy to look after.
Shar Peis	These dogs come from China. They are unusual, because they have a blue tongue.

12 What does the table show?
Tick your answer. *(1 mark)*

Q12

Where dogs live. ☐ How old dogs are. ☐

Breeds of dogs. ☐ Breeds of cats. ☐

subtotal

13 Which dogs come from Mexico?
Circle your answer. *(1 mark)*

Q1

Labradors Chihuahuas

Terriers Shar Peis

14 What three colours do Labradors come in? *(2 marks)*

Q1

a) ______________________________

b) ______________________________

c) ______________________________

15 Which is the most popular type of dog in the world today?
Tick your answer. *(1 mark)*

Q1

Terriers ☐ Chinese Crested ☐

Shar Peis ☐ Labradors ☐

One of the easiest ways to find out the breed of a dog is by looking at the shape of the face. Some dogs have very pointed faces, but others are more rounded. Another way to identify a breed of dog is by looking at the ears. Some dogs have pointed ears that stick up, but others have ears that droop down.

If you are choosing a dog for a pet, it is a good idea to visit a dog show, so you can see lots of dogs and talk to their owners.

16 Tick two ways, mentioned above, that can tell you a dog's breed. *(1 mark)*

Q16

By its size.	☐	By its colour.	☐
By the shape of its face.	☐	By its ears.	☐

17 What should you do if you are choosing a dog as a pet? *(2 marks)*

Q17

____

____

____

____

____

subtotal

Looking After a Pet Dog

Feeding

Dogs will eat both meat and vegetables. There are lots of different dog foods that you can buy in the shops, markets and pet stores.

You must remember not to give your pet dog too much food, as they will become fat and unhealthy.

Dogs should drink water every day. This should be in a clean bowl.

18 Tick three places where you can buy dog food. *(2 marks)* Q18

farms ☐ markets ☐

shops ☐ pet stores ☐

garden centres ☐ newsagents ☐

19 Why is it a bad idea to give your dog too much food? *(1 mark)* Q19

____

____

20 Why do you think the water should be in a clean bowl? *(1 mark)* Q20

____

____

In the Home

A pet dog will like to spend some time in the garden. There should be a fence around the garden so that the dog cannot run away. Some dogs can jump very well, so the fence should be quite high.

Dogs like sleeping in a comfy bed. They will need to have their own basket.

21 Where do dogs like sleeping?
Circle your answer. *(1 mark)* Q21

In a comfy bed. In a box.

On someone's knee. Under the stairs.

22 Why should a dog's garden have a fence? *(1 mark)* Q22

____

____

____

____

subtotal

23 Thinking of what you have read in this part of the test, do you think that the dog from the story "The Dog and the Bone" would make a good pet? Circle your answer.

Yes No

Why? Give two reasons. *(2 marks)*

Q23

a) ______________________________

____

____

____

____

b) ______________________________

____

____

____

____

END OF TEST

subto

KEY STAGE 1
Level 3

Reading
Test Paper

Reading

Moon Dancer
& Find out about Space

Level 3 Reading Test Paper

Moon Dancer
& **Find out about Space**

Instructions:

- find a quiet place where you can sit down and complete the test paper undisturbed
- make sure you have all the necessary equipment to complete the test paper
- read the Fiction Reading Material on pages 22–28 and then answer questions A, B and 1–14 on pages 36–41
- read the Non-Fiction Reading Material on pages 29–35 and then answer questions 15–20 on pages 41–42
- read the questions carefully
- answer the questions on the test paper
- go through and check your answers when you have finished writing

Time:

Take as long as necessary to complete the test paper but aim to complete it within 1 hour.

Note to Parents:

Check how your child has done using pages 83–84 of the Answers and Mark Scheme.

Page	37	39	41	42	Max. Mark	**Actual Mark**
Score	....	....	....	....	25	....

First name ____________________

Last name ____________________

Fiction Reading Material

moon dancer

For James Spader, most days were pretty normal. He was a normal boy, in a normal Year 3 class, at a normal school, in a normal town. Pretty normal really. Which is probably why the day he saved the Universe was anything but normal.

Ever since Christmas, James had been building a spaceship in his bedroom. It was made of all the leftover boxes that his family's presents had come in. His sister had got a massive television (much bigger than the one in his room, he had noticed) and its box had been the base.

On top of that stood a long thin white box, which used to contain his dad's hedge trimmer. He had managed to sneak four shoeboxes (who needs four pairs of shoes?) from his mum's room, and they became the rocket boosters he stuck to each side of the base. The last, and most crucial, part was the pointed, cone-shaped box that went right at the very top.

He knew straight away that he could make that one himself. Just last year his big brother, Alfie, had shown him how to make a giant cone by rolling up a large piece of card.

Once James had assembled the boxes and fixed them together with a combination of glue, sticky tape and bubble gum, he got to work on the inside. He added windows by cutting out sections of the base, a control panel with different coloured buttons to press and finally, a steering wheel.

At last, after three weeks of hard work and five minutes before bedtime, James's spaceship was finished. There was just one thing left to do.

"I proudly name you Moon Dancer," James said, as he carefully painted the words Moon Dancer onto the side of the spaceship.

With this done, James flopped down onto his bed, completely exhausted.

"Tomorrow," he muttered, trying to stay awake, "I'll take you for a test run, maybe to Mars."

As soon as the words left his mouth, James fell into a deep sleep.

"Captain Spader! Captain Spader!" The voice seemed to be coming from a million miles away. James grumbled and tried to roll over, but the hands that were gripping his shoulders wouldn't let him.

"Leave me alone. I'm trying to sleep," James mumbled.

"Captain Spader, you have to wake up! The Universe needs you!"

James sat up, still feeling groggy. He rubbed his eyes and sleepily turned to face the owner of the voice. Within an instant, all his sleepiness had left him. Standing right in front of him, gripping his shoulders, was an alien. James rubbed his eyes again, this time opening them really slowly, hoping that it was all a dream. But when he did open his eyes, nothing had changed. There was still a very worried-looking, little alien with green skin, big eyes and a round pot-belly standing by his bed.

Before James had a chance to say anything, the alien spoke.

"Captain Spader, I am very sorry for waking you. My name is Koko and I am from Jupiter. I came as quickly as I could. The whole Universe is in grave danger. There is a meteor heading straight for the Sun and you are the only one who can save us. On my planet we have heard of your bravery and courage. There is no one else who could save the Universe. You must come quickly!"

With that, Koko began tugging at James's arm, causing him to fall out of bed with a thump.

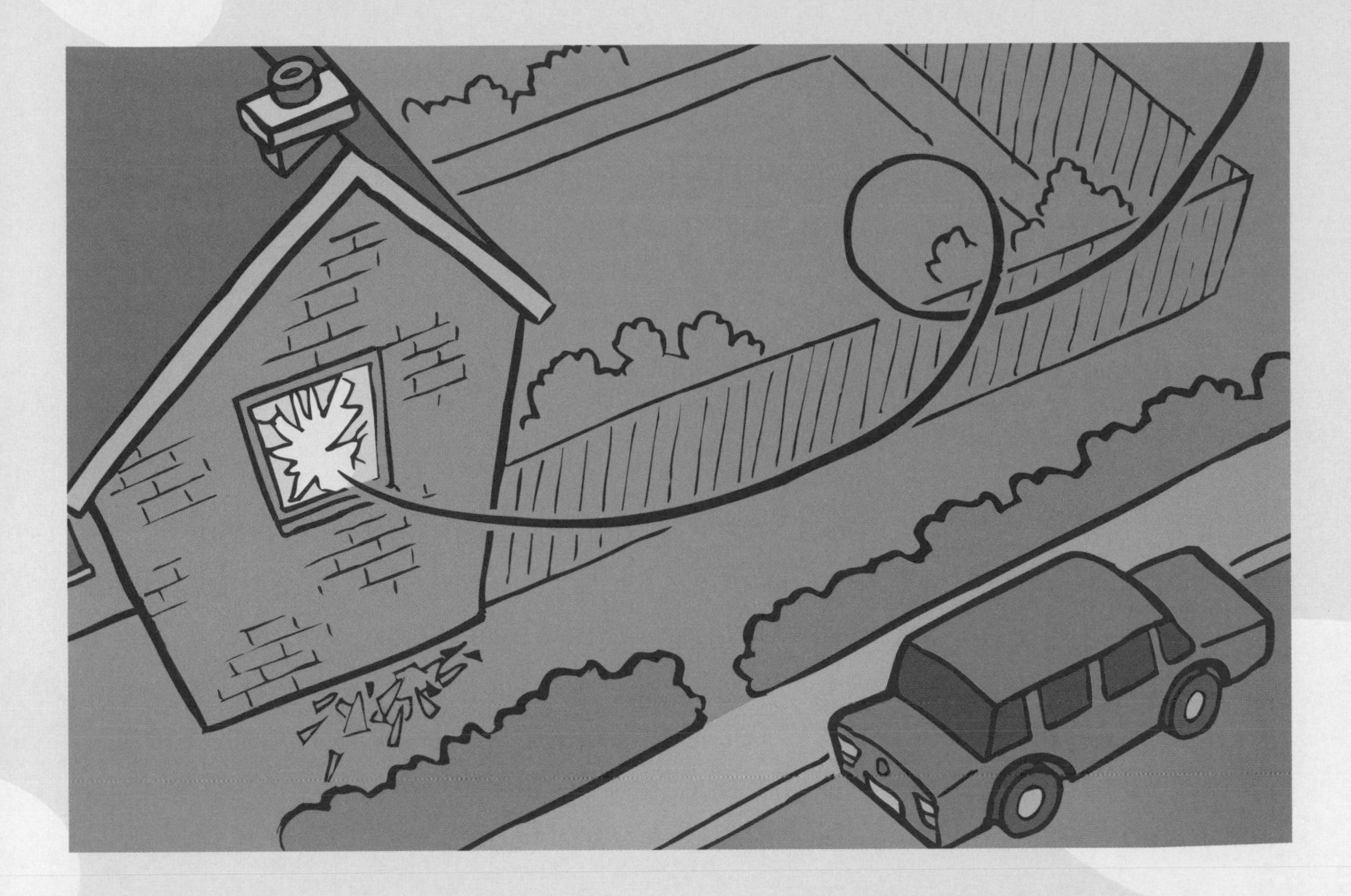

"I see you have your uniform on. That's good," Koko said, looking at James's Spiderman pyjamas.

"Erm, yes, well, you know," James said, still not sure whether he was dreaming or not.

Before he knew what was happening, James found himself bundled into the Moon Dancer and sitting behind his freshly painted control panel.

"Right, let's go!" said Koko, slamming the spaceship's door behind him.

James looked on with wide-eyed wonder as the control panel in front of him started to light up.

"Wow!" James said. He was starting to realise that this was no dream.

"Something wrong, Captain Spader?" Koko asked, a worried look creeping across his round face.

"Oh, er, nothing," replied James. "Just, you know, preparing for take-off."

James started pressing some of the flashing lights and at first nothing happened. Then slowly and steadily the Moon Dancer began to shake and rattle.

James could hear a low rumble coming from the four shoeboxes as the Moon Dancer's engines started up.

"Hold on tight!" he shouted above the thunder of the engines and pushed the nearest button to him. The Moon Dancer shot into the air and crashed out into the cold night through James's bedroom window.

"Mum's not going to like this!" James thought, as first his house, then his town and finally the Earth disappeared beneath him. He turned to Koko, who looked as if he might be sick very soon.

"Let's go and save the Universe!" Captain Spader said with a huge grin.

Find out about Space

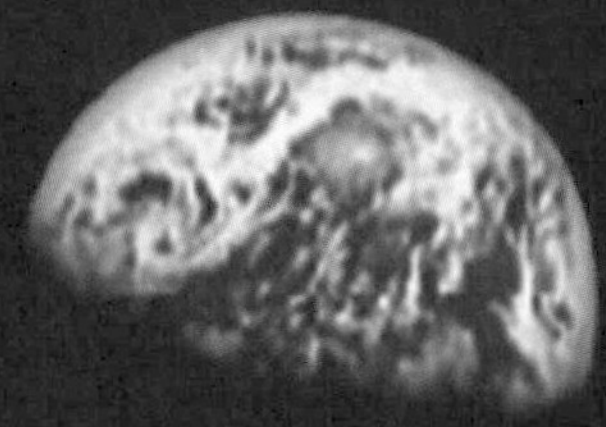

Space is what we see when we look into the night sky.

Space

The Sun is surrounded by eight planets in our solar system. In this part of the test you will be finding out more about the Sun, the Moon and the planets.

Sun facts

1 The Sun is a star. In the Universe there are billions of other stars too.

2 Like all stars, the Sun is a huge ball of glowing gas.

3 The Sun is a million times bigger than Earth.

4 The Sun is our nearest star.

The Sun and the eight planets are called the solar system.

The word solar means "belonging to the Sun".

The eight planets in our solar system are Mercury, Venus, Earth, Mars, Jupiter, Saturn, Uranus and Neptune.

Pluto is not called a planet because it is so small.

Facts about the planets and Pluto

1 Mercury, Venus, Earth and Mars are made from rock.

2 Mercury is the closest planet to the Sun.

3 Jupiter is the largest of all the planets.

4 Pluto is furthest away from the Sun. It is made of ice and rock, and is extremely cold.

All about the Moon

1. The Moon does not give any light of its own. It shines because some of the light given from the Sun shines onto it.
2. The Moon is made up of rock.
3. The Moon travels around the Earth. This is called an orbit.
4. When the Moon orbits Earth, it seems to change shape. This is because people on Earth can see different parts of the Moon lit up by the Sun.

Glossary

Orbit	When the Moon travels around the Earth.
Planets	Eight large objects in space. They all have their own name. Some are made from rock, others are made from gas.
Solar System	The Sun and all the other objects in space.
Universe	Space and all the things in space such as stars, suns, moons and planets.

Moon Dancer

Practice Questions

A What was everyday life like for James Spader?

____

____

____

B What had James been building in his bedroom?
Circle your answer.

A television A box

A spaceship A Christmas tree

Questions on pages 23 and 24 of the Level 3 Fiction Reading Material.

1 Where did James find the boxes for the rocket boosters?
Tick your answer. *(1 mark)* ☐ Q1

With his dad's hedge trimmer. ☐ In his brother's room. ☐

In his mum's room. ☐ In the garage. ☐

2 Why did James know straight away that he could make himself a cone-shaped box? *(1 mark)* ☐ Q2

____

____

____

3 Why do you think James was so exhausted, he *" flopped down onto his bed"*? *(1 mark)* ☐ Q3

____

____

____

subtotal ☐

Questions on pages 25 and 26 of the Level 3 Fiction Reading Material.

4 Why did the voice tell James he had to wake up? *(1 mark)*

Q4

5 *" James sat up, still feeling groggy."*

The author uses the word "groggy".
What do you think this means? *(1 mark)*

Q5

6 Why do you think James rubbed his eyes twice? *(2 marks)*

Q6

7 Why do you think Koko came to find James? *(1 mark)*

Q7

Questions on pages 27 and 28 of the Level 3 Fiction Reading Material.

8 What does Koko think James's pyjamas are? *(1 mark)* Q8

____

9 When did James begin to realise that he was not dreaming? *(1 mark)* Q9

____

____

10 Look at page 27. Which sentence tells you that James was amazed at the adventure? *(1 mark)* Q10

____

____

11 Why do you think James said "*Mum's not going to like this!*" as he flew away? *(2 marks)* Q11

____

____

____

____

subtotal

Questions on the whole of the Level 3 Fiction Reading Material.

12 Put these sentences in the right order by numbering them 1 to 6. The first one has been done for you. *(2 marks)* ☐ Q12

Moon Dancer began to shake and rattle. ☐

James had been building a spaceship in his bedroom since Christmas. 1

The control panel began to light up. ☐

James named his spaceship Moon Dancer. ☐

James was woken up by a strange voice. ☐

Koko explained how he needed Captain Spader to save the Universe. ☐

13 Do you think James was having a dream?
Circle your answer.

Yes No

Explain your answer. *(2 marks)* ☐ Q13

____

____

____

____

____

14 What would be a sensible ending for the story?
Tick your answer. *(1 mark)* ☐ Q14

James wakes up and finds he was dreaming. ☐

James saves the Universe and never returns home. ☐

James turns into an alien. ☐

Koko and James go on holiday. ☐

Find out about Space

Questions on pages 30 and 31 of the Level 3 Non-Fiction Reading Material.

15 What three things will you be finding out about in this part of the test? *(1 mark)* ☐ Q15

____

____

____

16 What is the Sun made of? *(1 mark)* ☐ Q16

____

____

____

subtotal

Questions on pages 32 and 33 of the Level 3 Non-Fiction Reading Material.

17 What does the word "solar" mean? *(1 mark)* Q17

____

18 a) Which planet is the largest? *(1 mark)* Q18

____

b) Why is Pluto so cold? *(1 mark)* Q18

____

Questions on pages 34 and 35 of the Level 3 Non-Fiction Reading Material.

19 What is it called when the Moon travels around the Earth? *(1 mark)* Q19

____

20 What is the glossary for? Tick one reason only. *(1 mark)* Q20

It explains meanings of words. ☐

It tells you what page you will find the word on. ☐

It teaches you to spell. ☐

It looks nice. ☐

END OF TEST

subtotal

KEY STAGE 1
Level 2

Reading
Test Paper

Reading

The Magic Sandcastle & How to Build a Sandcastle

Level 2 Reading Test Paper

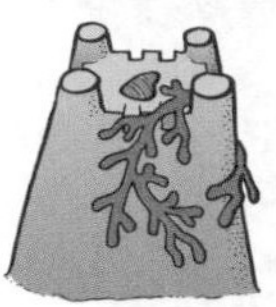

The Magic Sandcastle & How to Build a Sandcastle

Instructions:

- find a quiet place where you can sit down and complete the test paper undisturbed
- make sure you have all the necessary equipment to complete the test paper
- read the questions carefully
- answer the questions on the test paper
- go through and check your answers when you have finished writing

Time:

Take as long as necessary to complete the test paper but aim to complete it within 45 minutes.

Note to Parents:

Check how your child has done using pages 85–86 of the Answers and Mark Scheme.

Page	45	47	49	51	53	55	57	Max. Mark	**Actual Mark**
Score	....	....	....	....	....	....	....	30	....

First name ....

Last name ....

The Magic Sandcastle

Krishma and Tia were going to the seaside with their Aunt Mariah and Uncle Zakib during the long summer holidays.

They were dressed in bright blue swimming costumes and sparkling new jelly shoes. Both girls were very excited. It had been ages since they had played on the beach! Although they were only going for a few hours, Tia and Krishma had buckets and spades, rubber rings, a lilo, bats and balls. Their aunt and uncle could not believe how much they had brought with them.

Practice Questions

A Who were Krishma and Tia going to the seaside with? Circle your answer.

Their mum and dad Their brother and sister

Their aunt and uncle Some friends

B What were the girls wearing?

____

____

____

____

When they arrived at the seaside, Krishma and Tia gave each other a worried look.

"What's the matter, girls?"

"We thought you would have jumped out of the car by now," Zakib said.

"It's just that … it's starting to rain," Tia mumbled miserably.

"Don't worry about that," replied their aunt. "It's sea spray, that's all!"

Tia and Krishma were not convinced. Neither were Mariah and Zakib. Mariah tried to be cheerful.

"Let's go and sit in the café over there until the rain stops," she suggested.

1 Why is Tia feeling miserable? *(1 mark)*

Q1

____

____

2 What does Aunt Mariah say the rain is? *(1 mark)*

Q2

____

____

3 Where do they decide to go while the rain stops?
Circle your answer. *(1 mark)*

Q3

The shops A café

A beach hut The sea

subtotal

So Tia and Krishma walked miserably to the café. While they were waiting for their drinks to arrive, Krishma said she did not mind getting wet, if only she could feel the sand between her toes. So the two girls decided it might be fun after all to go onto the beach in the rain.

Their aunt and uncle told them to come back to the café in ten minutes, so the girls knew they did not have long to explore.

4 What did Krishma want to feel between her toes? *(1 mark)*

Q4

____

5 Why do you think the girls' aunt and uncle told them to come back in ten minutes? Give two reasons. *(2 marks)*

Q5

a) ______________________________

____

____

b) ______________________________

____

____

They ran through the wet sand down to the water's edge where they stood watching the waves crashing to the shore.

Tia saw something red poking out of the sand. She went to have a closer look and saw that it was an old spade, not nearly as good as her own one back in the car.

She did not mind though, and, with Krishma's help, she decided straight away to build a quick sandcastle. As the sand was wet they found that it stuck together much better than if it had been dry.

6 Write down what Tia found in the sand. *(1 mark)* ☐ Q6

---

7 What did Krishma and Tia decide to do?
Tick your answer. *(1 mark)* ☐ Q7

Go back to the café.	☐	Go in the sea.	☐
Collect shells.	☐	Build a sandcastle.	☐

subtotal

Tia and Krishma were pleased with their castle, but they suddenly remembered they should go back to the café.

"We can't go back before we've decorated the sandcastle," Tia whined. Krishma agreed and so quickly the girls ran to a nearby rock pool. They looked for a sparkling shell or a shiny stone, but nothing caught their eye.

"Here, this will have to do." Krishma pulled out a dirty stone and some slimy green seaweed.

8 Write down two things that the girls found in the rock pool. *(2 marks)*

Q8

a) ____

b) ____

9 Why do you think they wanted to decorate the sandcastle? *(2 marks)*

Q9

The castle looked rather strange, but it was the best they could do.

The girls returned to the café. By now the rain had stopped and the sun was shining in the distance.

It was time for drying out, so the four of them finished their drinks and returned to the beach.

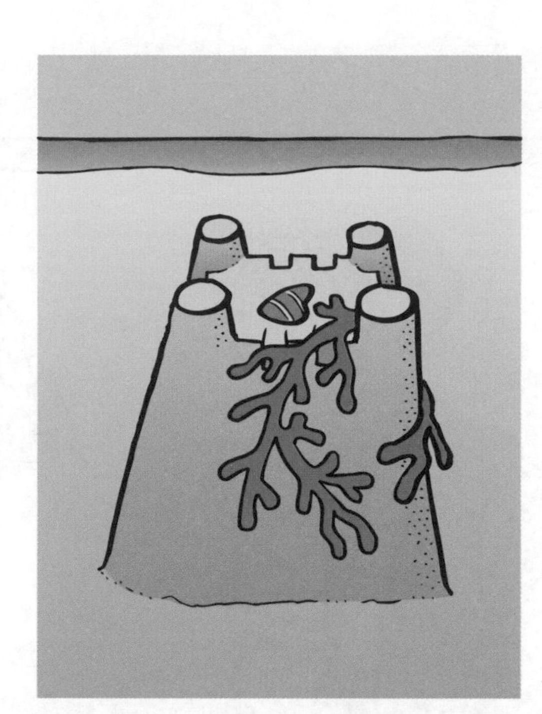

10 Circle the word that describes the sandcastle. *(1 mark)* Q10

strange	beautiful
tall	little

11 How had the weather changed? *(2 marks)* Q11

____

____

____

____

____

____

subtotal

However, something very strange had happened while they had been away. When Krishma and Tia saw their sandcastle, they could not believe their eyes! Instead of the dirty stone and the slimy seaweed, their castle was covered in bright, sparkling jewels! Zakib and Mariah were very impressed with the girls' work, but Tia and Krishma were astonished.

12 What was the castle decorated in now?
Circle your answer. *(1 mark)*

Q12

seaweed pebbles

jewels tinsel

"It must be magic!" said Krishma.

"No, someone must have helped us while we were away," Tia whispered, but there were no new footprints in the wet sand.

Well perhaps it was magic after all!

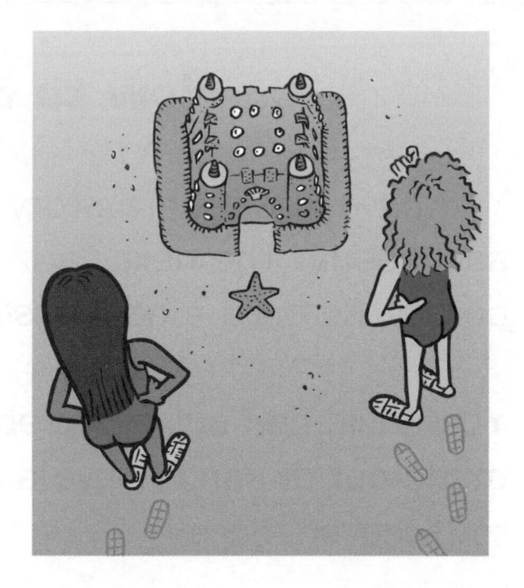

13 Which of the two girls thought it was magic that the jewels had appeared? *(1 mark)*

Q13

____

____

14 At the end of the story explain why the girls couldn't believe their eyes. *(2 marks)*

Q14

____

____

____

____

____

subtotal

How to Build a Sandcastle

You have just read a story about two girls who built a magic sandcastle. The next part of this test gives you some instructions on how to build a sandcastle yourself.

You could find out more about sandcastles and famous artworks made out of sand. Have a look on the Internet or visit the library to discover more.

Practice Questions

A What will you be reading in the next part of this test?
Tick your answer.

How to make magic.	☐	How to use the Internet.	☐
How to swim.	☐	How to build a sandcastle.	☐

B Which two places will help you find out more about artwork made from sand?

a) ____________________

b) ____________________

Instructions: How to Build a Sandcastle

You will need:

- Sand
- A little water
- A bucket
- A spade
- Shells to decorate

15 How many things do you need to build a sandcastle? *(1 mark)*

Q15

____

16 What do you use to decorate the sandcastle?
Circle your answer. *(1 mark)*

Q16

shells rocks

sand water

subtotal

Method:

1 First, find a good place to build your sandcastle. Make sure it is not too close to the sea!

2 Next, fill your bucket with sand.

3 Add a little water to stop the sandcastle crumbling and make sure the bottom is flat by smoothing it down.

4 Quickly turn the bucket of sand over. Be careful not to spill any!

17 Why do you have to add a little water? *(1 mark)* Q17

____

____

18 What must your sandcastle not be too close to?
Circle your answer. *(1 mark)* Q18

other sandcastles   people

shells   the sea

5 Pat the bottom of the bucket three times with your hand or the spade.

6 Very carefully lift the bucket away.

7 Decorate with beautiful shells.

19 How many times should you pat the bucket? *(1 mark)* Q19

____

____

20 Circle your answer. You should be careful not to: *(1 mark)* Q20

dig a hole　　　drop the spade

lose the shells　　　spill the sand

subtotal

Once you have made one sandcastle, you could try making others in a row. You might want to join these together by building a wall or a road out of sand.

You could be very clever and try building a palace or a castle for a king or queen.

Remember, though!

Be careful to build your sandcastle before the tide comes in!

21 What does the author suggest you could build to join other sandcastles together? *(2 marks)*

Q21

____

____

22 Which part of this practice paper have you enjoyed reading the most?

Tick one answer and give your reason. *(3 marks)* ☐ Q22

A The Magic Sandcastle ☐

B Instructions on how to build a sandcastle ☐

Why?

____

____

____

____

____

____

____

____

END OF TEST

subtotal ☐

KEY STAGE 1
Level 3

Reading
Test Paper

Reading

The Best Holiday Ever
& France

Level 3 Reading Test Paper

The Best Holiday Ever & France

Instructions:

- find a quiet place where you can sit down and complete the test paper undisturbed
- make sure you have all the necessary equipment to complete the test paper
- read the Fiction Reading Material on pages 59–66 and then answer questions A, B and 1–11 on pages 74–77
- read the Non-Fiction Reading Material on pages 67–73 and then answer questions 12–22 on pages 78–80
- read the questions carefully
- answer the questions on the test paper
- go through and check your answers when you have finished writing

Time:

Take as long as necessary to complete the test paper but aim to complete it within 1 hour.

Note to Parents:

Check how your child has done using pages 87–88 of the Answers and Mark Scheme.

Page	75	77	79	80	Max. Mark	**Actual Mark**
Score	....	....	....	....	25	....

First name ....

Last name ....

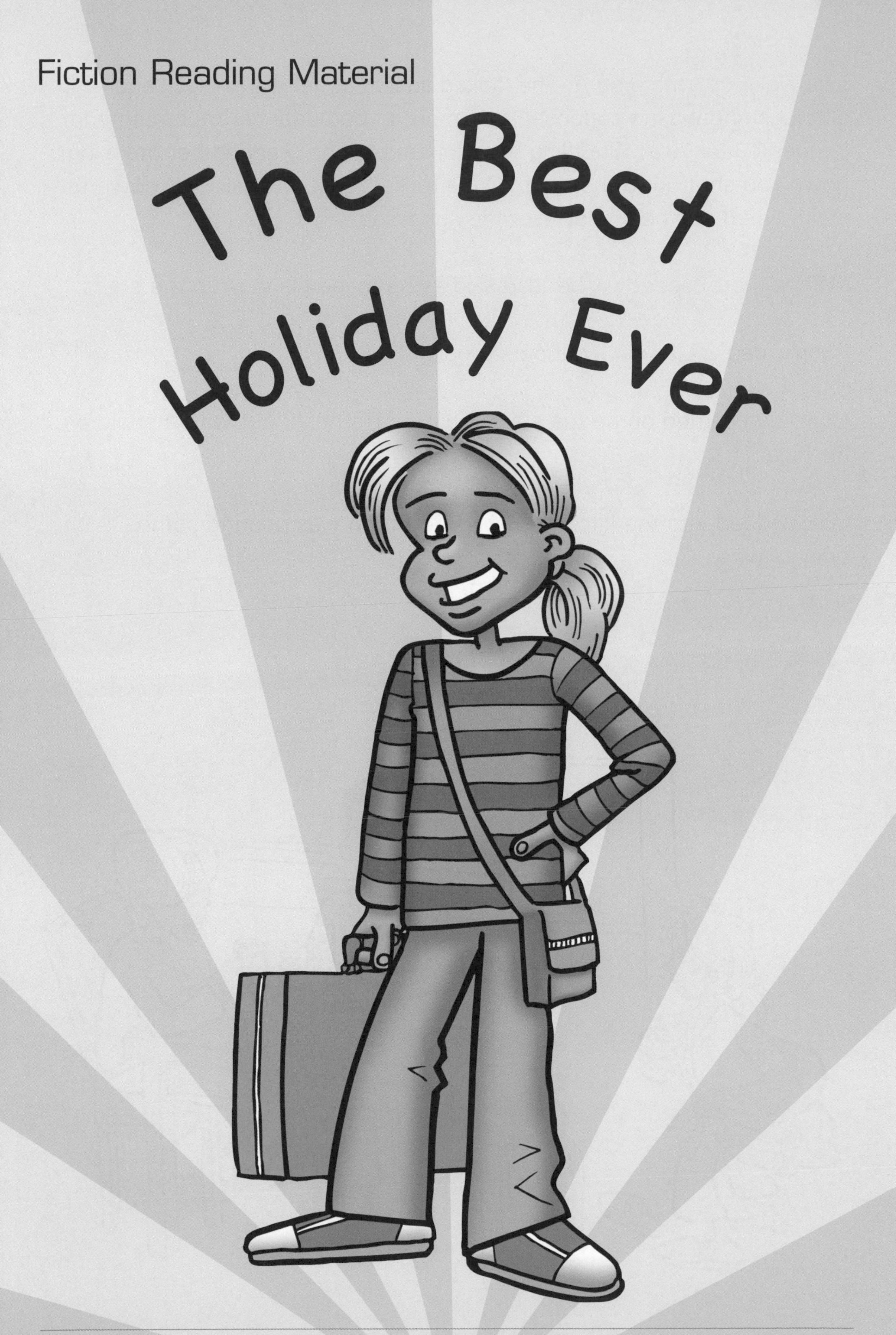
Fiction Reading Material
The Best
Holiday Ever

Lisa woke up with a start. She looked across at her alarm clock and although she wasn't supposed to get out of bed until her mum came in, jumped out anyway. Shuffling her slippers on, she grabbed her dressing gown and shot out of her room like a rocket. She was half way down the stairs when she nearly fell over the suitcases.

"Whoa there, speedy!" her dad said as he made his way up the stairs.

"Sorry, dad!" Lisa said without stopping.

Lisa's dad carried on up the stairs, shaking his head, but with a smile on his face.

Lisa skidded into the kitchen, just as her mum was pouring some orange juice.

"Morning, dear, would you like some?" her mum said, passing her a glass. "I suppose you're pretty excited about the summer holidays."

That was an understatement! Today was the first day of the summer holidays and to Lisa it felt like her birthday and Christmas combined.

Last year her mum and dad had taken her to Spain, where she spent nearly every day playing in the pool. The year before that they had gone to Greece and the year before that they went to Portugal.

Where would it be this year? Lisa was hoping for Disneyland. Her friend Laura had been and said it was the best place ever.

"Well?" Lisa asked, unable to contain her excitement any longer. "Where are we going on holiday?"

"Oh yes, right," her mum said. She was very good at pretending to be calm. "This year, your dad and I thought we might drive down to France."

For a moment Lisa was sure her mum had just said they were going to drive to France.

"Pardon?" Lisa said.

"I said, we are going to drive to France. It will be lovely, dear. We've booked a really nice farmhouse to stay in. It's in the middle of the countryside."

No Disneyland, no beach and no airport. All of a sudden, Lisa wanted to climb back into bed and sleep for the rest of the summer holidays.

They had been driving for nearly two hours and Lisa's bad mood hadn't lifted. Before they left the house Lisa's dad had tried to cheer her up by telling her how much fun they would have, but Lisa wasn't convinced. So she had sat in the back of the car in silence, with a huge frown on her brow. What would she tell Laura when she got back to school? No doubt Laura had been on a wonderful holiday, to somewhere hot with big beaches, somewhere you had to get on an aeroplane to get to.

The only good part about this trip was that Lisa could now smell the sea. Just then they turned a corner and Lisa saw the biggest ship she had ever seen in her life.

"What's that?" she asked, her face pressed up against the car window.

"Why, that's the ferry," said her dad, smiling. "We have to drive the car onto the ferry, then the ferry takes us across the Channel."

"What's the Channel?" Lisa asked.

"It's the name for the sea in between England and France," Lisa's dad replied.

"Cool!" Lisa said, looking at the ferry.

Lisa's mum and dad looked at each other and smiled.

Lisa spent the entire ferry journey outside, watching as the huge ship pushed its way through the water on its way to France. She watched as the white cliffs of Dover disappeared into the distance and shrieked with laughter as she threw bits of her cheese and onion sandwich for the passing seagulls to catch in their beaks. Time flew by so fast that it wasn't long before they were back in the car and driving off the ferry.

Although the next part of the journey took a really long time, Lisa didn't mind. She played a game with her mum as they tried to spot the names of the towns they passed through. Lisa got a good start as she spotted Calais, the name of the town the ferry had docked in. The tricky part was pronouncing the names correctly, but her dad helped her. One of the names she saw on a sign she knew straight away.

"Hey, that sign says 'Paris'!" Lisa exclaimed.
"We've learnt about that in school. It's the capital city of France."

"Nice one, Lisa!" her dad said.
"You can have two points for that."

By the time they got to the farmhouse it was nearly dark. Lisa was feeling pretty tired, but as soon as she saw where they would be staying, all her weariness disappeared. The farmhouse was beautiful. It was an old stone building surrounded by meadows on one side and a huge wood on the other. Lisa could imagine herself running through the tall grass in the meadows, playing hide and seek with her mum and then building a tree house in the wood with her dad.

"Oh yeah," her mum said, "there's also a pool around the back."

"This is going to be the best holiday ever!" Lisa said, rushing inside.

Her mum and dad looked at each other and smiled.

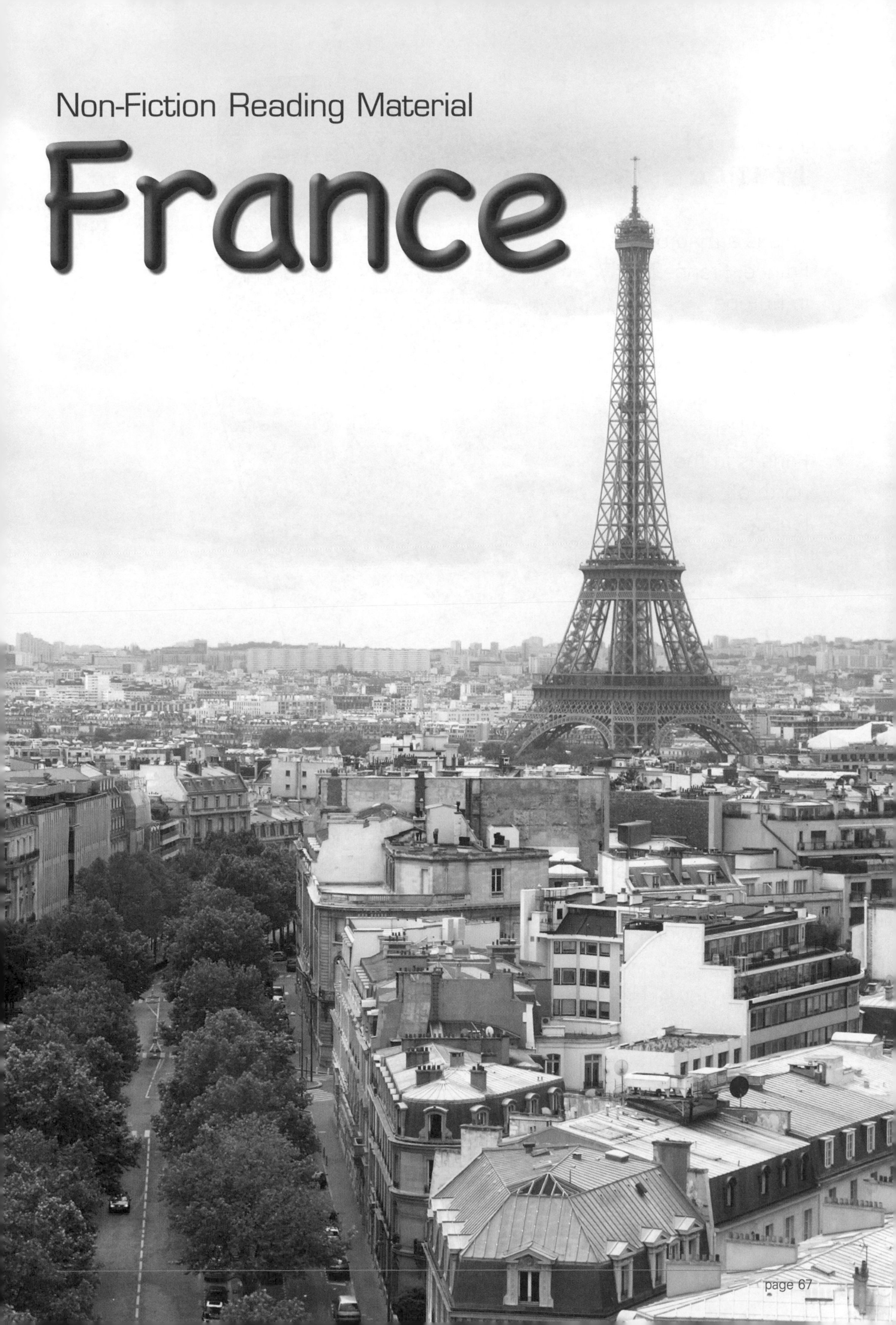

Non-Fiction Reading Material

France

Map of France

This is a map of France. France is in Europe.

The capital city of France is called Paris. Paris is in the north of France.

All about Paris

There are lots of places of interest in Paris and tourists from all around the world come to visit this beautiful capital city.

People often take a boat trip along the River Seine. From the river you can see the Eiffel Tower.

The Eiffel Tower is a very tall monument. It was built in 1889 by a man called Gustave Eiffel. You can climb up the Eiffel Tower and take photographs of Paris from the top.

Six million people a year visit the Eiffel Tower.

The French Flag

The French flag has three stripes – red, white and blue. The flag is called the "Tricolore". This means three colours.

Festivals and Special Occasions

There are many festivals and carnivals in France. The French people love to dress up and celebrate all sorts of special occasions.

The carnival at Nice in the south of France is the biggest. It lasts for twelve days.

French parties usually have fun fairs, music, decorated floats and magnificent firework displays.

French Food

In France, people buy a lot of their food such as meat, fruit, vegetables and cheese from local markets.

France is famous for its cheeses. They are often eaten with fresh bread.

Some popular French cheeses are Camembert, Roquefort and Brie.

French people also love to eat fresh bread and pastries.
It is very popular to have croissants for breakfast, served with a range of jams and hot chocolate.

French Specialities

1. Frogs' legs taste a bit like chicken. They are usually lightly fried in garlic and you eat them with your fingers.

2. Snails are very popular in France. They are served in their shells and eaten with a special fork.

3. Crêpes are pancakes. You can eat them with a savoury or a sweet filling.

Read the recipe below to find out how to make your own crêpes.

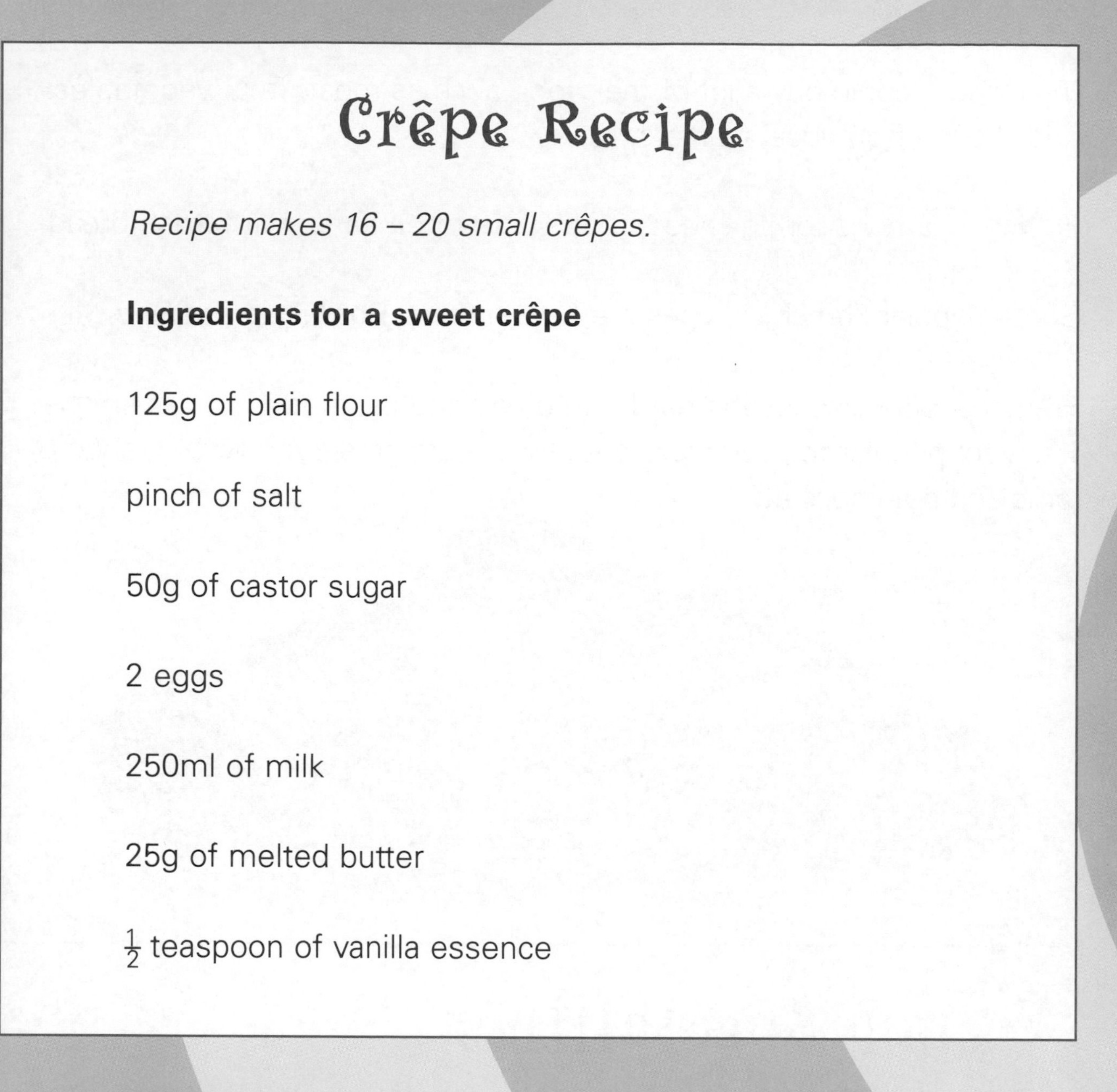

Crêpe Recipe

Recipe makes 16 – 20 small crêpes.

Ingredients for a sweet crêpe

125g of plain flour

pinch of salt

50g of castor sugar

2 eggs

250ml of milk

25g of melted butter

$\frac{1}{2}$ teaspoon of vanilla essence

Method

1. Sift the flour, salt and sugar into a mixing bowl.
2. Add the eggs and half of the milk.
3. Mix the mixture to make a smooth batter.
4. Stir in the rest of the milk, butter and vanilla essence.
5. Beat for two minutes.
6. Grease the frying pan and place over a high heat until it is really hot.
7. Pour the batter into the pan.
8. Cook both sides.
9. Serve with a sweet filling such as orange, chocolate or fresh fruits.

The Best Holiday Ever

Practice Questions

A How did Lisa leave her room?

B What was Lisa so excited about?
Circle your answer.

Christmas | Her birthday

Breakfast | The summer holidays

Questions on pages 60, 61 and 62 of the Level 3 Fiction Reading Material.

1 Where was Lisa hoping her family were going on holiday? *(1 mark)* Q1

____

2 Lisa's mum said they were going to France.
What sort of place were they going to stay in?
Tick your answer. *(1 mark)* Q2

A hotel ☐ A farmhouse ☐

A tent ☐ A castle ☐

3 What does Lisa think about their holiday plans when she first hears them? *(1 mark)* Q3

____

____

4 Why do you think Lisa wants to climb back into bed and sleep? *(1 mark)* Q4

____

____

subtotal

Questions on pages 63 and 64 of the Level 3 Fiction Reading Material.

5 Why do you think Lisa was worried about what she would tell her friend Laura? *(2 marks)*

Q5

____

____

____

6 What does Lisa's dad say the name of the sea between France and England is called? *(1 mark)*

Q6

____

____

____

Questions on pages 64, 65 and 66 of the Level 3 Fiction Reading Material.

7 Why do you think the ferry journey flew by for Lisa? *(1 mark)*

Q7

____

____

____

8 What helped pass the time in the car? *(1 mark)*

Q8

9 Why do you think Lisa's weariness disappeared when she saw where she was staying? *(1 mark)*

Q9

Questions on the whole of the Level 3 Fiction Reading Material.

10 To start with, Lisa did not want to go to France and she was in a bad mood. When in the story did her mood change? *(1 mark)*

Q10

11 At the end, her mum and dad smiled at each other. Why do you think they did this? *(1 mark)*

Q11

subtotal

France

Questions on pages 68 and 69 of the Level 3 Non-Fiction Reading Material.

12 a) What is the name of the French flag? *(1 mark)* Q12

____

b) What does this name mean? *(1 mark)* Q12

____

13 What is the name of the river that runs through Paris? *(1 mark)* Q13

____

14 Write down one fact about the Eiffel Tower. *(1 mark)* Q14

____

Questions on pages 70 and 71 of the Level 3 Non-Fiction Reading Material.

15 What lasts for twelve days? Tick your answer. *(1 mark)* Q15

All festivals	☐	The carnival in Nice	☐
Music	☐	All carnivals	☐

16 What food is often served with fresh bread in France? *(1 mark)* Q16

---

17 How are frogs' legs usually cooked? *(1 mark)* Q17

Questions on pages 72 and 73 of the Level 3 Non-Fiction Reading Material.

18 How can you find out how to make French crêpes? *(1 mark)* Q18

---

19 What sort of sugar does the recipe suggest you use? *(1 mark)* Q19

---

subtotal

Questions on the whole of the Level 3 Non-Fiction Reading Material.

20 How many crêpes does the recipe on page 72 make? *(1 mark)*

Q2

____

21 If you wanted to find out more about food specialities in France, which page would be most useful? *(1 mark)*

Q2

____

22 This is a piece of non-fiction writing. Here is a feature of non-fiction text. List two more features. *(2 marks)*

Q2

Pictures

____

____

END OF TEST

subto

Answers and Mark Scheme

Set A – Level 2 Reading Test Paper

The Dog and the Bone

Practice Questions

A greedy

B The dog stopped outside the butcher's shop to get a closer smell of the meat/To smell the meat.

1 The dog was looking at the different meats and tasty bones. *(1 mark)*

2 The dog felt hungry/extremely hungry. *(1 mark)*

3 He snatched a bone. *(1 mark)*
Note to parent *– check that your child understands that they must only tick one box – remind them that there is only one correct answer.*

4 The dog held the bone between his teeth, so he would not lose it/so he did not drop it. *(1 mark)*

5 A stream A bridge His reflection *(2 marks)*
Any two of these answers for 2 marks

6 The dog growled at the water, so he could get the bone/to frighten the dog in the water so he would drop the bone. *(1 mark)*

7 When the bone fell in the water, the dog began to cry/he cried. *(1 mark)*

8 He could not reach the bone. *(1 mark)*

9 beautiful tasty *(2 marks)*
Note to parent *– remind your child that this is worth 2 marks and that they should tick two boxes.*

10 We know the dog was upset as he walked home, as his tail was down and his face was covered in tears/he had been crying. *(2 marks)*
Note to parent *– with questions like this, encourage your child to look for detail in the passage and actual examples. Encourage them to pick the actual words from the story.*

11 Be happy with what you have. *(1 mark)*

All About Dogs

Practice Questions

A dogs

B Information A guide

12 Breeds of dogs *(1 mark)*

13 Chihuahuas *(1 mark)*

14 Yellow Black Chocolate *(2 marks)*
2 marks for all 3 correct, 1 mark for 1 or 2 correct

15 Labradors *(1 mark)*
Note to parent *– remind your child to keep looking back at the information in the table.*

16 By the shape of its face. By its ears. *(1 mark)*

17 You should visit a dog show / see lots of dogs. Talk to other owners. *(2 marks)*
1 mark for each correct reason

18 shops markets pet stores *(2 marks)*
2 marks for all 3 correct, 1 mark for 1 or 2 correct

19 They will become fat / unhealthy. *(1 mark)*

20 The water should be in a clean bowl, so the dog does not become ill / to avoid germs / to keep the water fresh. *(1 mark)*

21 In a comfy bed. *(1 mark)*
Note to parent *– when looking at the questions, explain to your child that all of these answers could be correct but they must read the text and use the information given.*

22 The garden should have a fence, so that the dog cannot run away. *(1 mark)*

23 Answer can be Yes or No – *1 mark for each reason* *(2 marks)*
Yes = Because dogs are popular animals / he learnt his lesson in the end / he will not be greedy again.
No = He was greedy and unkind / he would not be easy to look after / he might run away or go wandering again.

Set A – Level 3 Reading Test Paper

Moon Dancer

Practice Questions

A Everyday life was very normal / normal.

B A spaceship

1 In his mum's room. *(1 mark)*

2 He knew because his brother Alfie had shown him how to make one last year. *(1 mark)*

3 James was so exhausted because it was five minutes before his bedtime / he had worked really hard and been busy. *(1 mark)*

4 The voice told him to wake up, because the Universe needs him / he has to save the Universe. *(1 mark)*

5 He means tired / sleepy. *(1 mark)*

6 He rubbed his eyes twice to see if he was dreaming or to try and wake himself up. Because he could not believe what was happening. *(2 marks)*
1 mark for each answer (maximum 2 marks)

7 Koko came to find James as he had heard about James's bravery and wanted him to help. *(1 mark)*

8 Koko thinks James's pyjamas are his uniform. *(1 mark)*

9 When he was in the spaceship and the control panel began to light up. *(1 mark)*

10 James looked on with wide-eyed wonder as the control panel in front of him started to light up. *(1 mark)*

11 Because he was escaping through his bedroom window at night.
Because his mum would be worried about him. *(2 marks)*
1 mark for each answer

12 6, 1, 5, 2, 3, 4 *(2 marks)*
2 marks for all correct, 1 mark for 3, 4 or 5 correct
***Note to parent** – it is important that your child can order and re-tell stories. You could spend time practising this with them through other texts.*

13 Answer can be Yes or No – *1 mark for each reason* *(2 marks)*
Yes = It would never normally happen / aliens don't come into bedrooms / you cannot really fly in a cardboard box / James was in bed asleep.
No = Koko knew all about James / Science has proved aliens may exist / James didn't think he was dreaming.
***Note to parent** – it does not matter whether your child puts yes or no – they are awarded marks for their reasoning.*

14 James wakes up and finds he was dreaming. *(1 mark)*

Find out about Space

15 The Sun, the Moon and the planets. *(1 mark)*

16 The Sun is made of glowing gas. *(1 mark)*

17 Solar means belonging to the Sun. *(1 mark)*

18 a) Jupiter *(1 mark)*
b) It is furthest away from the Sun / it is made of ice. *(1 mark)*

19 It is called an orbit. *(1 mark)*

20 It explains meanings of words. *(1 mark)*
Note to parent *– your child may be asked questions like this during school assessments to ensure they understand the features of a non-fiction text, e.g. glossary, index, contents, captions, etc ...*

Set B – Level 2 Reading Test Paper

The Magic Sandcastle

Practice Questions

A Their aunt and uncle

B They were wearing bright blue swimming costumes / jelly shoes. (Either answer is acceptable.)

1 Tia is feeling miserable because it is starting to rain. *(1 mark)*

2 Aunt Mariah says the rain is sea spray. *(1 mark)*

3 A café *(1 mark)*

4 Krishma wanted to feel the sand between her toes. *(1 mark)*

5 The girls were told to be back in ten minutes, so they would be back by the time their drinks arrived.
So they wouldn't be on their own for too long.
So they wouldn't get too wet in the rain.
So Mariah and Zakib would not be worried. *(2 marks)*
Any two of these answers for 2 marks

6 An old spade *(1 mark)*

7 Build a sandcastle. *(1 mark)*
Note to parent *– remind your child to tick only one answer.*

8 A dirty stone Some seaweed *(2 marks)*

9 They wanted to make it look nice To finish it off To be proud of it *(2 marks)*
Any two of these answers for 2 marks
Note to parent *– this is a question where your child has to give their own reasoning – point out that because the question is worth two marks, they should give two reasons.*

10 strange *(1 mark)*

11 Award 2 marks if a change in the weather is mentioned, i.e. it was raining and it is now sunny / it was bad weather and is now sunny. Do not give any marks for the answer 'sunny' – there must be understanding of the change. *(2 marks)*

12 jewels *(1 mark)*

13 Krishma thought it was magic. *(1 mark)*

14 1 mark awarded for answer which gives one statement, e.g. the sandcastle was covered in jewels.
2 marks awarded for answer which gives further explanation, e.g. the seaweed had been replaced by jewels / the sandcastle looked much better than before. *(2 marks)*

How to Build a Sandcastle

Practice Questions

A How to build a sandcastle.

B The library The Internet

15 You need five things. *(1 mark)*

***Note to parent** – after your child has answered the question, check that they understood that they needed to count the number of bullet points.*

16 shells *(1 mark)*

17 You add a little water to stop the sandcastle crumbling. *(1 mark)*

18 the sea *(1 mark)*

19 Pat the bucket three times. *(1 mark)*

20 spill the sand *(1 mark)*

21 You could build a wall or a road to join them together. *(2 marks)*
1 mark for each correct answer

22 A or B *(3 marks)*
Marks awarded for valid reason. *1 mark for each relevant point. Maximum 3 marks*
Suggestions: The Magic Sandcastle, because it was a mystery / I liked the characters / the ending was good / it used some good descriptions, etc.
Instructions on how to build a sandcastle, because I have learnt something / there were interesting facts / I liked the way it was set out in bullet points, etc.
***Note to parent** – it is a good idea to ask your child this frequently when they are reading stories or other non-fiction texts – encourage them to give reasons for their preferences. This will develop their skills in sharing opinions.*

Set B – Level 3 Reading Test Paper

The Best Holiday Ever

Practice Questions

A She left her room like a rocket / very fast.

B The summer holidays

1 She was hoping her family were going to Disneyland. *(1 mark)*

2 A farmhouse *(1 mark)*

3 She thinks she doesn't like them / it will be boring / it will not be as good as her previous holidays. *(1 mark)*

4 She wants to pretend the news is a bad dream / to forget about the news. *(1 mark)*

5 She is worried, because Laura always went on brilliant holidays.
Laura might tease her for not going on an aeroplane. *(2 marks)*
Award 1 mark for each point

6 The name of the sea is the Channel. *(1 mark)*

7 The ferry journey flew by, because she was having fun / she was enjoying herself / she was very busy. *(1 mark)*

8 Playing a game where they had to spot French towns helped pass the time in the car.
(Do not accept 'playing games' – the answer needs to be more specific.) *(1 mark)*

9 Her weariness disappeared because the farmhouse was beautiful.
She liked the meadows and the wood. *(1 mark)*
1 mark for either statement

10 Her mood changed when she saw the ferry. *(1 mark)*
Note to parent *– ensure your child gives a specific point in the story.*

11 They were pleased Lisa was happy / they secretly knew Lisa would like it / they were smiling at how Lisa's mood had changed. (1 mark)
Note to parent *– this is an inference question – encourage your child to think beyond what is actually being said in the story. It is a good idea to discuss characters and their actions with your child.*

France

12 a) The Tricolore *(1 mark)*
b) Three colours *(1 mark)*

13 The River Seine *(1 mark)*

14 It is a tall monument / it was built in 1889 / Gustave Eiffel built it / you can climb to the top / it is near the Seine / six million visitors a year. *(1 mark)*
Any correct answer for 1 mark

15 The carnival in Nice *(1 mark)*

16 Cheese *(1 mark)*

17 They are usually lightly fried in garlic. *(1 mark)*

18 Read the recipe and method on pages 72 and 73. *(1 mark)*

19 Castor sugar *(1 mark)*

20 The recipe makes between 16 and 20 crêpes. *(1 mark)*
Note to parent *– remind your child that some of the questions may be about headings, sub-headings or titles.*

21 Page 71 *(1 mark)*

22 Any of the following:
bullet points, captions, headings, sub-headings, titles, index, glossary, contents. *(2 marks)*
1 mark for each answer (maximum 2 marks)

Letts

KS1 Success

PRACTICE TEST PAPERS

Writing & Spelling

Laura Griffiths

Contents

Introduction

Introduction

Instructions on using the Practice Test Papers

Understanding Assessment

What is assessment?
Teacher assessment will form the main part of your child's result at the end of Key Stage 1 (at the age of 7). However, tests and tasks help to validate the teacher's own assessment.

What are the children tested on?
All children study the National Curriculum from Year 1. At the end of Year 2, the tests will assess your child's knowledge, skills and understanding in the programmes of study that they have followed from Year 1.

In English the programme of study covers three areas:
English 1: Speaking and Listening
English 2: Reading
English 3: Writing

What tests will my child take?
Teacher assessment for seven-year-olds covers:

- reading
- writing
- speaking and listening
- maths
- science

These assessments take account of how your child performed in Key Stage 1 tasks and tests. The tasks and tests cover:

- reading
- writing (including handwriting and spelling)
- maths

The tasks and tests are informal and can be taken at a time the school chooses, although they usually take place towards the end of Year 2. The tasks and tests last for less than three hours altogether and the results help to inform the teacher's overall assessment of your child. No statutory testing is carried out at Key Stage 1.

Can my child fail a test?
It is important that children understand they are not going to 'pass' or 'fail' the test – it will just show what they have learned and what they can do.

Preparing your Child for Tests

These practice test papers prepare your child for school tests by giving them the confidence of knowing the sort of questions they will experience.

These practice test papers will also help you to assess how your child is doing at school. They will give you an indication of your child's strengths and weaknesses, and how you can help them.

How can you improve your child's score?

- Mark the papers.
- Look at what your child got wrong and talk it through with them.
- Let your child do the test again.
- Remember, keep practising the things they are weaker at. For example, if it is joining their handwriting or using punctuation, work further on these.
- Try to encourage your child not to throw away marks, by reading a question carefully and checking their answer.

About these Practice Test Papers

In this book, there are three separate sets of writing and spelling tests.

The writing tests comprise two writing tasks, one longer and one shorter. The tasks cover different styles of writing.

For your child to achieve their best result, it is advisable to give them only one task in a day.

The long task should take approximately 45 minutes, not including planning, and the short task should take approximately 30 minutes, not including planning.

The Long Writing Task

The specific writing tasks vary each year. The long task is usually selected from the following text types.

1 **A personal recount:** This writing would be the child recounting something they have done at school – for example, "The day we visited the police horses".

2 **Informative writing:** This is factual writing – for example, information about a dinosaur.

3 **Instructions:** This would be an explanation of how to do or make something – for example, a moving puppet.

4 **Extending and adapting stories:** This would include continuing a story – for example, writing the story ending or writing a story using the same characters from a familiar story but within a different setting.

5 **Letter writing:** This could be a letter to a character in a story (for example, Goldilocks), or to a famous person (for example, Florence Nightingale).

6 **Expressing opinions:** This could be writing about whether the toys that Grandma played with when she was a child are more exciting than those of today.

How to Administer the Long Task to your Child

Test A: Long Task – Letter writing

Read Gran and Grandpa's letter to your child. Discuss the content of the letter.

To help children think through their own ideas, it might be useful to ask them the following questions to support their writing:
a) Where do you think Gran and Grandpa live?
b) Do you think Gran and Grandpa miss James?
c) Why are Gran and Grandpa asking about his school?

Direct your child to the planning sheets and encourage them to write down their ideas.

Your child should not spend long on the planning sheets. It is just to support their writing and will not be marked.

When your child has completed their planning sheets and understood what the task is, they should begin writing the letter on a separate sheet of paper.

Most children can complete this piece of writing in 45 minutes and this timing should not normally be exceeded.

Your child should write independently, trying their best with spelling, handwriting and punctuation.

Encourage your child to use interesting vocabulary which is appropriate to the task, reader and purpose.

Test B: Long Task – Continuing a story

Read the story to your child and check they understand it. To help children think through their own ideas, it might be useful to ask them the following questions to support their writing:

a) Where is Katie going?
b) What might happen at the party?
c) How will your story end?

When your child understands the task, follow the same process as Test A. Direct them to the planning sheets to complete and then ask them to write their story on a separate sheet of paper.

Test C: Long Task – Story writing

Read the story of the hare and the tortoise to your child. Discuss the moral at the end of the story and ask them to give you ideas as to what it means.

Explain the task to them and discuss other animals that could be used.

When your child has an idea and feels confident with the writing, follow the same process as Tests A and B.

Assessing your Child's Score for the Long Task

You will need to assess three aspects of your child's writing:

1 Sentence structure.
2 Punctuation.
3 Composition and effect.

Each of these three aspects of your child's writing is divided into a number of bands which represent the level of achievement that your child has attained. For guidance, please refer to pages 49 and 50 of the Answers and Mark Scheme.

Please use the marking sheet on page 11 to record the marks. Where there is a choice of two or three different marks, use your judgement to decide if your child has fully achieved the objective or just partially.

When marking your child's writing, you must decide into which band it fits best. To help you decide which band your child's work falls into, please refer to the annotated children's writing on pages 51 to 54 of the Answers and Mark Scheme.

The Short Writing Task

In school assessments, the specific writing task varies each year. The short task could be selected from the following text types.

1 **Report writing:** This is writing about something the child has read. They would be expected to use appropriate vocabulary and to sequence ideas correctly.

2 **Writing instructions:** This could be, for example, how to play a game, how to bake a cake or writing rules.

3 **Note-taking:** This is writing where the child is expected to make simple notes from non-fiction texts, using headings, sub-headings and captions.

How to Administer the Short Task to your Child

Test A: Short Task – Postcard

Remind your child of the letter they wrote to Gran and Grandpa. Explain the task of writing a postcard. To support your child with their content, it is a good idea to give them an opportunity to share their thoughts orally.

Remind your child before they begin that they must write independently, making a sensible guess at any unknown spellings. Encourage them to use punctuation to make the meaning of their writing clear.

When they are ready to begin, direct them to the template of the postcard on page 21. They may like to put an address on the card, although this will not be marked.

Test B: Short Task – Recipe for making a cake

Before you start this activity, it will help your child if you show them a recipe for making a cake, or better still actually make one with them! This will give your child a good idea of the ingredients and method.

Direct your child to the planning sheet. Read the headings together and ask them to write down their ideas. Remind them not to spend too long on the planning.

When your child has completed the planning sheet, they should begin writing the recipe.

Test C: Short Task – Writing rules

Administer this test in the same way as Test A. Remind your child of the story of the hare and the tortoise. Discuss races and what rules are needed. Ask your child to write down rules for a successful school sports day.

All of the short tasks should take approximately 30 minutes to complete.

Assessing your Child's Score for the Short Task

You will need to assess two aspects of your child's writing:

1 Sentence structure and punctuation.
2 Composition and effect.

These two aspects of your child's writing are divided into a number of bands which represent the level of achievement that your child has attained. For guidance, please refer to pages 55 and 56 of the Answers and Mark Scheme.

Please use the marking sheet on page 12 to record the marks. Where there is a choice of two different marks, use your judgement to decide if your child has fully achieved the objective or just partially.

When marking your child's writing, you must decide into which band it fits best. To help you decide which band your child's work falls into, please refer to the annotated children's writing on pages 57 to 59 of the Answers and Mark Scheme.

The Spelling Test

Your child will be tested on 20 words. Some of these words will be easier than others.

What to do

Give the spelling test to your child. Explain that they will hear the story read aloud and when they come to a missing word they need to write the correct spelling.

Encourage your child to follow the passage on their test sheet, while you read the complete passage at a speed appropriate to your child.

Then read the passage again, more slowly this time, pausing at the gaps to allow your child to fill in the missing words. The first word is a practice and no marks are awarded for this word.

The words in bold type are the spellings that your child needs to write down.
Begin the test. You may repeat the target spellings once.

When your child has completed the spelling test, add up the total score (out of 20, excluding the practice question). Your child must spell the entire word correctly to gain a mark.

Marking the Tests and Assessing Levels

You can fill in your child's results in the tables below. Please refer to guidance and writing examples in the pull-out Answers and Mark Scheme for how to assess your child's performance.

Long Task Marking Sheet

Band A Sentence structure	Band B Punctuation	Band C Composition and effect

Total marks for the Long Task:

Set A: ___________ Set B: ___________ Set C: ___________

Short Task Marking Sheet

Band D Sentence structure and punctuation	Band E Composition and effect

Total marks for the Short Task:

Set A: ___________ Set B: ___________ Set C: ___________

Handwriting

There is no separate test to assess your child's handwriting. This makes it much easier! A score out of 3 will be given, by assessing the handwriting from the writing tasks. Please refer to page 60 of the Answers and Mark Scheme.

Spelling Test Marking Sheet

Your child will have a score out of 20. Use the table below to convert this score into a mark out of 7.

Number of correct words	0–3	4–7	8–11	12–14	15–16	17–18	19–20
Marks	1	2	3	4	5	6	7

The Overall Writing Level

You will now have separate scores for your child's writing. Insert these scores into the grid below.

	Set A	Set B	Set C
Long Task (out of 18)			
Short Task (out of 12)			
Handwriting (out of 3)			
Spelling (out of 7)			
Total score (out of 40)			

Please use the table below to convert your child's score into a National Curriculum level.

Score out of 40	National Curriculum level
0–8	Level 1 not achieved
9–17	Level 1 achieved
18–22	Level 2c achieved
23–27	Level 2b achieved
28–32	Level 2a achieved
33–40	Level 3 achieved

Please note: these tests are only a guide to the level your child can achieve and cannot guarantee the same level is achieved at Key Stage 1.

How well has my child done in these tests?

The results show whether or not your child has reached the expected National Curriculum level at the age of 7.

Level	Aged 7
Level 1	Below average
Level 2 Level 2c Level 2b Level 2a	At level expected
Level 3	Excellent
Level 4	Exceptional
Level 5	
Level 6	
Level 7	
Level 8	

What do the levels mean?

When your child's writing paper is marked, the correct marks are collated to give your child an overall score. This score is then matched to a National Curriculum level.

The government target for pupils at the end of Year 2 is to achieve Level 2. Some pupils will be working below this level and achieve Level 1, whilst other pupils will be working above the expected level and achieve Level 3.

KEY STAGE 1
Levels 1–3

Planning Sheets & Writing Tasks

Writing

Planning Sheets & Writing Tasks

Dear James

Instructions:

- see page 6 (Long Writing Task) and page 8 (Short Writing Task) for details on how to administer the writing tasks
- find a quiet place where your child can sit down and complete the writing tasks undisturbed
- make sure your child has all the necessary equipment to complete the writing tasks
- make sure your child knows how to plan each task using the planning sheets
- when your child has completed the planning sheet, go through it together
- your child then begins the writing task on a separate sheet of lined paper
- check how your child has done using pages 49–62 of the Answers and Mark Scheme

Time:

Take as long as necessary but aim to complete the Long Writing Task in 45 minutes and the Short Writing Task in 30 minutes.

	Max. Mark	**Actual Mark**
Score	33	....

First name ....

Last name ....

Dear James

Dear James

Instructions: This stimulus material is very similar to what your child will be given in school tests. The idea of it is to set the scene of the task and help your child to become inspired with their writing. You should read the stimulus material to your child. Ensure they understand it.

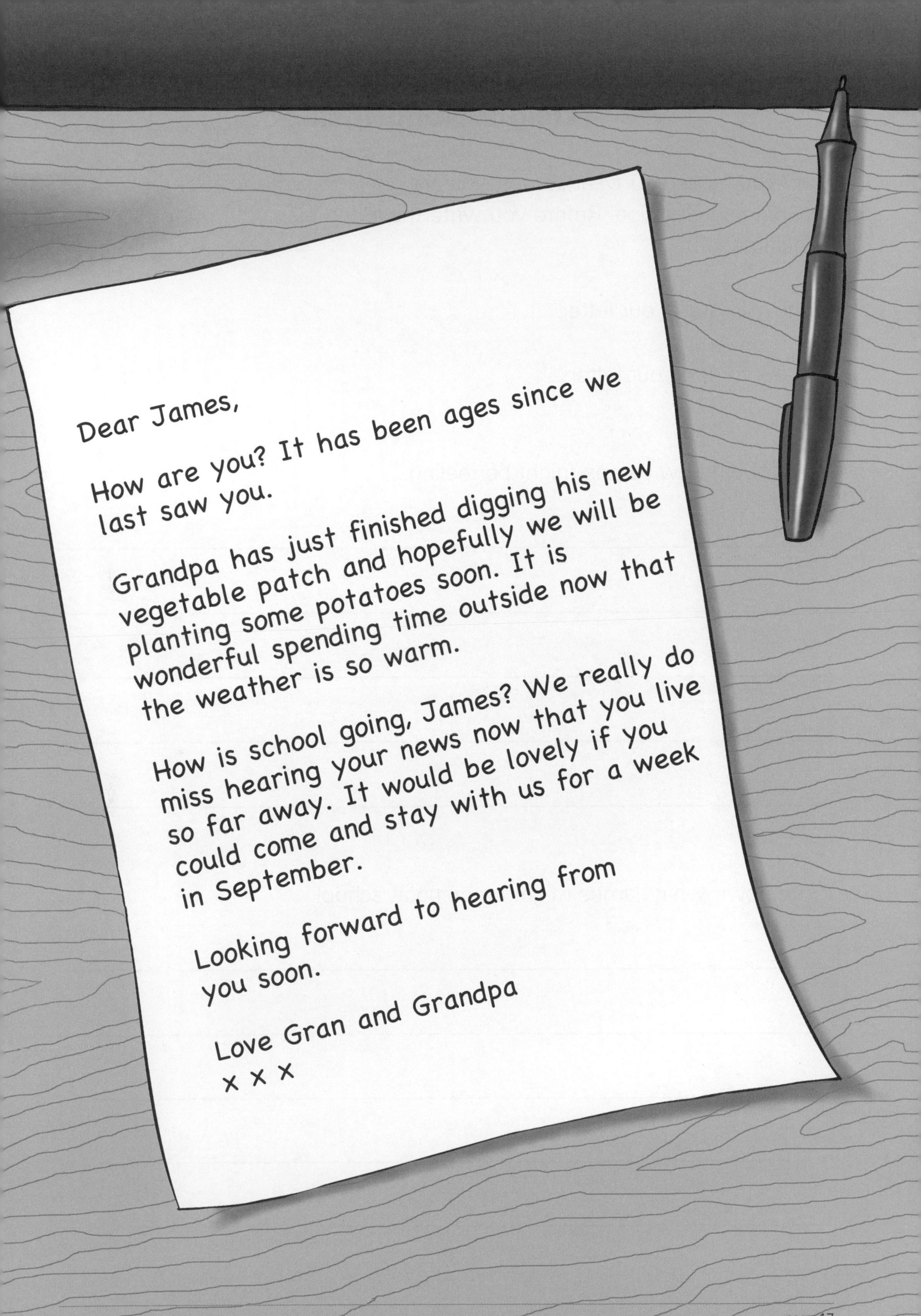

Dear James,

How are you? It has been ages since we last saw you.

Grandpa has just finished digging his new vegetable patch and hopefully we will be planting some potatoes soon. It is wonderful spending time outside now that the weather is so warm.

How is school going, James? We really do miss hearing your news now that you live so far away. It would be lovely if you could come and stay with us for a week in September.

Looking forward to hearing from you soon.

Love Gran and Grandpa

x x x

Long Writing Task

Now you have read *Dear James*, you are going to write a letter replying to Gran and Grandpa. Before you write the letter, plan your reply by thinking about:

1 how to start your letter

2 how to end your letter

Write down how James might be feeling.

Write down what James might be doing at school.

Write down an answer to the invitation to stay in September.

Write down three questions James could ask Gran and Grandpa.

Read through your plan and think about what you have written. Now write your letter.

Short Writing Task

You are going to imagine James has gone to stay with his Gran and Grandpa and he is sending a postcard back home. You are going to write the postcard.

Before you write the postcard, plan what you will write by thinking about:

One exciting thing James has done.

____

____

____

What the weather is like.

____

____

____

How James feels.

____

____

____

Read through your plan and think about what you have written. Now write the postcard.

Writing Template for the Postcard

KEY STAGE 1
Levels 1–3

Spelling Test Paper

Spelling

Pete's Big Feet

Spelling Test Paper

Pete's Big Feet

Instructions:

- see page 10 for details on how to administer the test
- find a quiet place where you can sit down with your child
- make sure you have all the necessary equipment to complete the test paper
- read the short piece of text on page 63 to your child twice in its entirety
- during the first reading, your child should not write anything on the test paper
- during the second reading, pause after each word to be tested (shown in bold type), to enable your child to write the word in the gap on the test paper
- see page 64 for the spelling test mark conversion chart

Time:

Take as long as necessary to complete the test paper.

	Max.	**Number of words correct**
Score	20	....

First name ________________________________

Last name ________________________________

1

Say "Hi!" to Pete. He is ___**ever**___ so sweet. *(practice question)*

He is ______________ mean and ______________ smiles at ______________ he meets.

He remembers to say ______________ and thank you, too. At ______________, Pete likes to help ______________ ______________ his street. He tidies up garden weeds and sweeps floors for them.

When it is sunny, Pete ______________ to fish at Wheat Field Stream.

But his favourite meal is not fish. It is lean meat ______________ peas. And if he has a treat, it has to be cheese.

You see, Pete likes the same ______________ as ______________ ______________.

He loves ______________ with mates and ______________ movies. He tries to be neat and tidy in his best ______________ jeans.

Above his knees, Pete ______________ like ______________ you ______________ meet. But ______________ the knees, he makes some squeal.

"Are those real feet?" some say.

Others ask "Can I have a feel? Wow, ______________ feet are unreal!"

You see, Pete has big, no, huge, no, giant-sized feet!

KEY STAGE 1
Levels 1–3

Planning Sheets & Writing Tasks

Writing

Planning Sheets & Writing Tasks

Katie

Instructions:

- see pages 6–7 (Long Writing Task) and page 8 (Short Writing Task) for details on how to administer the writing tasks
- find a quiet place where your child can sit down and complete the writing tasks undisturbed
- make sure your child has all the necessary equipment to complete the writing tasks
- make sure your child knows how to plan each task using the planning sheets
- when your child has completed the planning sheet, go through it together
- your child then begins the writing task on a separate sheet of lined paper
- check how your child has done using pages 49–62 of the Answers and Mark Scheme

Time:

Take as long as necessary but aim to complete the Long Writing Task in 45 minutes and the Short Writing Task in 30 minutes.

	Max. Mark	**Actual Mark**
Score	33	....

First name ....

Last name ....

Katie

Instructions: This stimulus material is very similar to what your child will be given in school tests. The idea of it is to set the scene of the task and help your child to become inspired with their writing. You should read the stimulus material to your child. Ensure they understand it.

"Hurry up, Katie, you're going to be late!" shouted Katie's mum from downstairs.

Katie was in the middle of getting ready for a very special day. Today was her friend's birthday party.

Everyone in the class was going to be there and she was really looking forward to it.

Katie was going to wear her very best dress and some sparkling new, pink shoes.

When she was finally ready, she tiptoed downstairs where her mum was waiting rather impatiently.

Katie climbed into the car, remembering to check that her dress did not get creased!

Katie felt very excited and throughout the journey she told her mum about the plans.

"There is going to be a magician, party food, hats and games. There's even going to be a bouncy castle," Katie sang merrily.

Katie said goodbye to her mum cheerily and ran into the party.

Long Writing Task

Now you have read *Katie*, you are going to continue the story and write about what happens at the party. Before you write the story, plan what you will write by thinking about:

Who is at the party.

What games Katie and her friends play.

What happens to the magician.

Remember:

1 to write a good beginning

2 to write a clear ending

Read through your plan and think about what you have written. Now write your story.

Short Writing Task

You are going to write a recipe for a birthday cake. Before you write the recipe, plan what it will include by thinking about:

Preparation time: ______________________________

Cooking time: ______________________________

Number of people it will serve: ______________________________

Ingredients: ______________________________

____

____

____

____

____

Method: ______________________________

____

____

____

____

____

Read through your plan and think about what you have written. Now write the recipe.

Set
B

KEY STAGE 1
Levels 1–3

Spelling Test Paper

Spelling

Musical Statues

Spelling Test Paper

Musical Statues

Instructions:

- see page 10 for details on how to administer the test
- find a quiet place where you can sit down with your child
- make sure you have all the necessary equipment to complete the test paper
- read the short piece of text on page 63 to your child twice in its entirety
- during the first reading, your child should not write anything on the test paper
- during the second reading, pause after each word to be tested (shown in bold type), to enable your child to write the word in the gap on the test paper
- see page 64 for the spelling test mark conversion chart

Time:

Take as long as necessary to complete the test paper.

	Max.	**Number of words correct**
Score	20	....

First name ....

Last name ....

Instructions on how to play musical statues.

You will ____need____: *(practice question)*

Music

A stereo

A ____________ to ____________

Lots of ________________________

An adult to judge

1 Wait ____________ the music to ____________.

2 ____________ the music ____________, dance around the room.

3 As ____________ as the music ____________, stand as still as ________________________ can.

4 Remember not to ____________ at all – be ____________ not to blink your ____________ or ____________!

5 An adult will ____________ around the room ____________ for anyone who is moving.

6 If you are caught moving, then you are ____________ and you must sit at the side of the room.

7 The winner is the last ____________ still ____________.

8 ____________ luck!

KEY STAGE 1
Levels 1–3

Planning Sheets & Writing Tasks

Writing

The Hare and the Tortoise

Planning Sheets & Writing Tasks

The Hare and the Tortoise

Instructions:

- see pages 6–7 (Long Writing Task) and page 8 (Short Writing Task) for details on how to administer the writing tasks
- find a quiet place where your child can sit down and complete the writing tasks undisturbed
- make sure your child has all the necessary equipment to complete the writing tasks
- make sure your child knows how to plan each task using the planning sheets
- when your child has completed the planning sheet, go through it together
- your child then begins the writing task on a separate sheet of lined paper
- check how your child has done using pages 49–62 of the Answers and Mark Scheme

Time:

Take as long as necessary but aim to complete the Long Writing Task in 45 minutes and the Short Writing Task in 30 minutes.

	Max. Mark	**Actual Mark**
Score	33	....

First name ....

Last name ....

The Hare and the Tortoise

Instructions: This stimulus material is very similar to what your child will be given in school tests. The idea of it is to set the scene of the task and help your child to become inspired with their writing. You should read the stimulus material to your child. Ensure they understand it.

Once upon a time, there lived two very different animals. One of these animals was a grumpy hare and the other was a very clever and gentle tortoise.

One day, in the middle of summer, Hare and Tortoise met each other.

"Why are you always so slow?" Hare asked Tortoise.

"I like my pace," Tortoise replied. "Besides, being fast isn't always everything!"

"Oh yes it is," Hare said.

The two animals argued for a while, then Tortoise suddenly came up with an idea.

"Listen, Hare," he said. "Why don't we have a race? Let's see who will win. How about over the hill and back?"

Hare roared with laughter! "You want to have a race with me? You haven't got a chance!"

"We'll see," Tortoise smiled.

So the next day Tortoise and Hare met for their race. Hare started running immediately. He went away very fast and it wasn't long before he was way out in front.

"Why am I rushing?" Hare thought to himself.

"That silly, slow tortoise won't have even started yet! I know, I'll sit by this tree and have a rest for a while."

So the hare sat down and closed his eyes. He fell into a very deep sleep and eventually began snoring.

Meanwhile, the tortoise was plodding on, and after a very long time he crept past the sleeping hare. Tortoise went on his way, over the hill and back again.

Hare suddenly woke up and tried to race to catch the tortoise up but he'd left it too late. The tortoise had won the race!

The moral of this story is "slow and steady wins the race".

Don't rush things!

Long Writing Task

Now you have read *The Hare and the Tortoise*, you are going to write a similar story, using different animals. Remember in your story that the moral is "slow and steady wins the race". Before you write your story, plan what you will write by thinking about:

Your two animals.

1 ____

2 ____

Where they race.

____

____

____

Who wins.

____

____

____

____

How they feel at the end of the race.

Read through your plan and think about what you have written. Now write your story.

Short Writing Task

Imagine the hare and the tortoise take part in your school sports day.

Write some rules to tell them both how to take part and behave without arguing.

Your first might be:

1 You must do as you are told the first time.

2

3

4

5

6

KEY STAGE 1
Levels 1–3
Spelling Test Paper

Spelling

Dear Cinderella

Spelling Test Paper

Dear Cinderella

Instructions:

- see page 10 for details on how to administer the test
- find a quiet place where you can sit down with your child
- make sure you have all the necessary equipment to complete the test paper
- read the short piece of text on page 64 to your child twice in its entirety
- during the first reading, your child should not write anything on the test paper
- during the second reading, pause after each word to be tested (shown in bold type), to enable your child to write the word in the gap on the test paper
- see page 64 for the spelling test mark conversion chart

Time:

Take as long as necessary to complete the test paper.

	Max.	Number of words correct
Score	20	....

First name ________________________

Last name ________________________

Dear ______________ Cinderella, *(practice question)*

We are ______________ sorry for being horrible to ______________ when you lived with us. We ______________ you a lot now that you ______________ in the palace with the prince.

We have to do all the cleaning, ______________ and ironing now. It is ______________ not fair! The other day our wicked mother ______________ made us mop the ______________.

Last week we had to hang all the washing outside in the ______________ and as soon as we had finished our work it began to rain. We felt very ______________, especially as our ______________ dresses had ______________ ruined!

We are both hoping that one ______________ we will meet a prince just like you did. When is the prince having ______________ ball? We will make sure we wear the most beautiful glass slippers in the whole world.

We would ______________ it if you could ______________ and visit us sometime because we are quite lonely. We would love to hear all about your new life in the palace. Do you have servants and maids?

Maybe we ______________ come and ______________ for you one day?

Love ______________

The Ugly ______________

xxx

Notes

Answers and Mark Scheme

Writing Tasks

Mark Scheme for the Long Tasks

Sentence structure

Assessment focuses: Vary sentences for clarity, purpose and effect.

Band	Description	Mark
A1	Meaningful words and phrases, some of them expressing ideas in sentence-like structures. Some parts of the writing may be abbreviated or disjointed.	*1 mark*
A2	Mainly simple, grammatically accurate statements, often starting with personal subject and past tense action verbs. Writing is often speech-like (e.g. "we did playing"). Repeated pronouns (e.g. "I", "we", "they") or subject nouns (e.g. "the cake ...." "the cake"). Use of simple verbs (e.g. "went", "got", "said"). A mixture of simple and compound sentences joined by simple connectives to ensure events are chronologically ordered (e.g. "then we played pass the parcel, then everyone gave me presents, then we had tea"). Some modification of unspecific nouns (e.g. "chocolate cake", "good game", "different presents"). Use of time adverbials (e.g. "first", "then", "after").	*2–3 marks*
A3	Simple connectives (e.g. "and", "but", "then", "so") link clauses into chronological sequence (e.g. "Your letter was lovely, but I'm at school in September, so maybe in August"). Mainly compound sentences, sometimes explaining relationships between ideas (e.g. "Katie had a great birthday because all her friends were there"). Nouns sometimes modified by adjectives (e.g. "slow, lazy tortoise") and verbs modified by adverbs (e.g. "he ran quickly"). Variation in word order and/or position of clauses (e.g. "First our teacher put the music on and we passed the parcel around, then the music stopped").	*4 marks*

Punctuation

Assessment focuses: Write with technical accuracy of syntax and punctuation in phrases, clauses and sentences.

Band	Description	Mark
B1	Some awareness shown of how full stops are used.	*1 mark*
B2	Sentences sometimes demarcated by both capital letters and full stops. Other punctuation may be used (question marks, exclamation marks).	*2–3 marks*
B3	Full stops, capital letters and commas in lists mostly accurate. Question marks and exclamation marks may be used.	*4 marks*

Composition and effect

Assessment focuses: Write imaginative, interesting and thoughtful texts. Produce writing which is appropriate to task, reader and purpose. Organise and present whole texts effectively.

Band	Description	Mark
C1	Some recognisable letters or groups of letters relating to the task. Writing has to be mediated by child, teacher or parent to be understood.	*1–2 marks*
C2	Writing refers to the task and describes actions and events clearly. Events are linked as simple sequences.	*3–4 marks*
C3	Writing relates to the task, with actions detailed in a chronological sequence. There is a simple opening (e.g. "one sunny morning, a mouse was running across the field"). A general concluding statement (e.g. "The mouse was pleased and they ran to the end of the race together"). Some detail included to expand on basic information (e.g. "Next week I'm taking my friends to an athletics tournament. We're playing for a cup"). Some technical vocabulary may be used (e.g. "medal", "finishing tape", "competitors").	*5–7 marks*
C4	Writing exhibits a clear sequence of events, demonstrating a sound opening and ending. The features and stages of the task are clear to the reader. Paragraphing and other organisational features may be evident. Some evidence of viewpoint or personal comment on the task.	*8–10 marks*

Example Writing for the Long Task – "Dear James"

Band A Sentence structure: Band A3, *4 marks*

Band B Punctuation: Band B3, *4 marks*

Band C Composition and effect: Band C4, *9 marks*

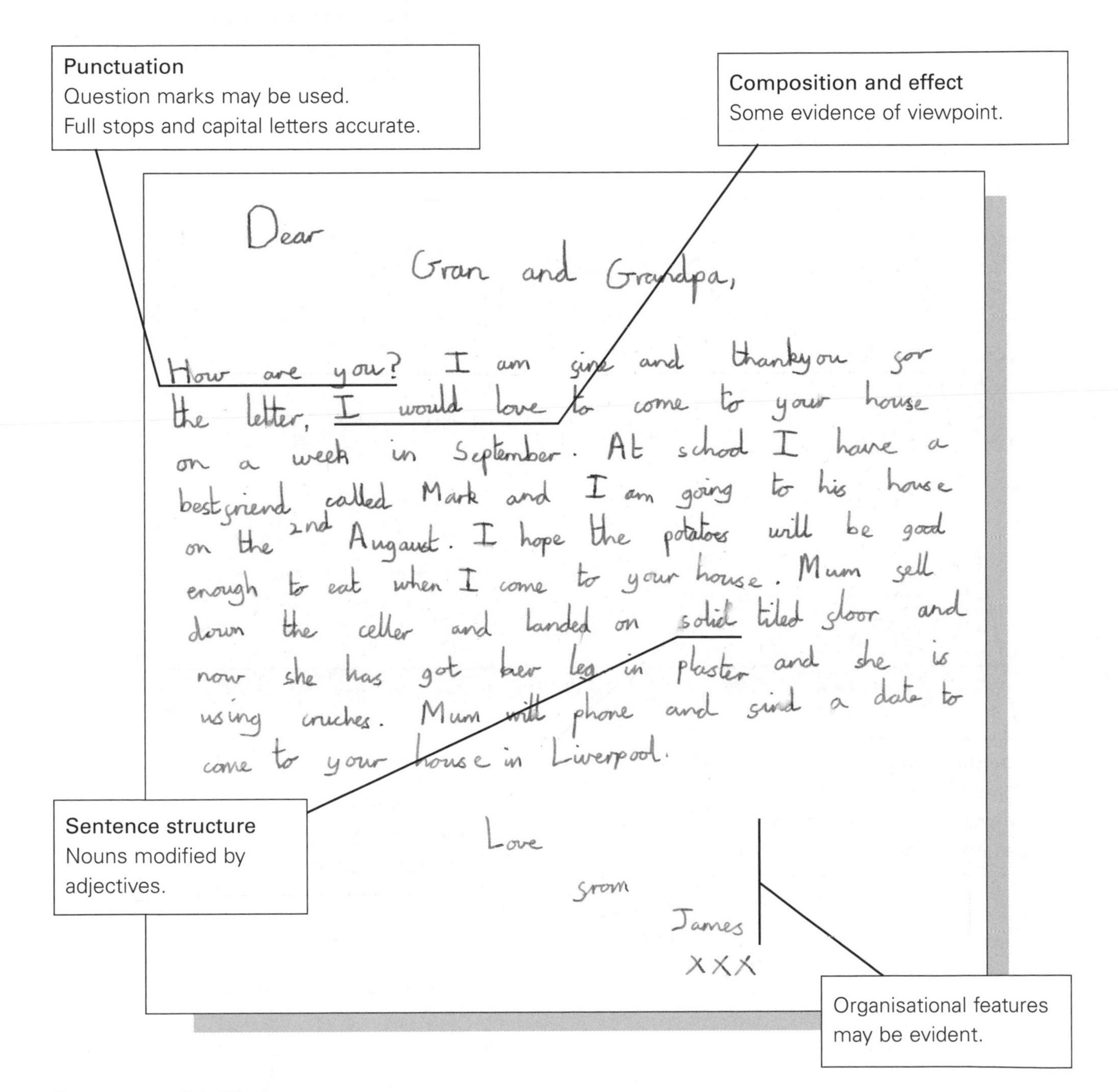

Dear

Gran and Grandpa,

How are you? I am fine and thankyou for the letter, I would love to come to your house on a week in September. At school I have a bestfriend called Mark and I am going to his house on the 2nd Augaust. I hope the potatoes will be good enough to eat when I come to your house. Mum fell down the celler and landed on solid tiled floor and now she has got her leg in plaster and she is using cruches. Mum will phone and find a date to come to your house in Liverpool.

Love

from

James

XXX

Summary of writing

- Writing exhibits a clear sequence of events. Sound opening and end.
- Detail included – e.g. "come to your house in Liverpool".

Total marks: 17

Example Writing for the Long Task – "Dear James"

Band A Sentence structure: Band A1, *1 mark*

Band B Punctuation: Band B1, *1 mark*

Band C Composition and effect: Band C1, *1 mark*

Sentence structure
Some parts of the writing may be disjointed.

Composition and effect
Some recognisable letters. Writing has to be mediated to be understood.

Punctuation
Some awareness shown of how full stops are used.

Total marks: 3

Example Writing for the Long Task – "Katie"

Band A Sentence structure: Band A2, *3 marks*

Band B Punctuation: Band B2, *3 marks*

Band C Composition and effect: Band C2, *4 marks*

Sentence structure
Action verb in the past tense.

The day Katie went to a party
once there lived a little girl her name was
called Katie She was realy exsited at
the party. She saw Bob. Betty and Bill Bob
was very good very good indead he was exstreamly
kind betty was very kind like Bob there was
a... magician he Jugled with fire! Bill was very
nasty a horrible at the end of the party it was So
good she did not want to Leave then Katie Said
"ok I'll go home" good girl said her mum and they
Lived hapely ever after.

Punctuation
Use of other punctuation.

Sentence structure
Mixture of simple and compound sentences with clauses joined by 'then'.

Summary of writing
- Writing refers to the chosen activity – e.g. "magician".
- Events are described – e.g. "magician he juggled with fire".

Total marks: 10

Example Writing for the Long Task – "Katie"

Band A Sentence structure: Band A2, *2 marks*

Band B Punctuation: Band B2, *2 marks*

Band C Composition and effect: Band C3, *7 marks*

Sentence structure
Sentence structures often speech-like.

Composition and effect
Some evidence of viewpoint.
Technical vocabulary may be used.

One bright sunny ~~morng~~ Afternoon geogia arrived at the patry.
We did playing on the big boney castle, ball cave, swiming pool, swing.
Then we played pass the parcel katie lost I won. but I gave the
present to Geogia. Then evey one gave me presents I was surised
I opend them ~~I~~ liked The party. evey one liked it. when
it was time to go i was upset I didnt want
to leave so i creyed. I went to the kutten were
I got a goody bag. I looked in side. I ate my
cake and went home.

Punctuation
Sentences sometimes demarcated by both capital letters and full stops.

Sentence structure
Repetition of pronoun I.

Summary of writing

- There is a simple opening and concluding statement.

Total marks: 11

Mark Scheme for the Short Tasks

Sentence structure and punctuation

Assessment focuses: Vary sentences for clarity, purpose and effect. Write with technical accuracy of syntax and punctuation in phrases, clauses and sentences.

Band	Description	Mark
D1	Meaningful words and phrases, some of them expressing ideas in sentence-like structures. Some parts of the writing may be abbreviated or disjointed. Some awareness shown of how full stops are used.	*1 mark*
D2	Mainly simple, grammatically accurate statements or questions. Some clauses joined by and/then (e.g. "Add the eggs and the flour. Mix together, then put in the bowl, then put in the oven"). Some sentences demarcated by capital letters and full stops or question marks.	*2–3 marks*
D3	Consistent use of appropriate format. Nouns modified by adjectives (e.g. "the kind man", "the shining gold medal"). Clauses linked by connectives such as "and", "but", "so". Details are specific (e.g. times of events, place names). Full stops and capital letters mostly accurate, with capital letters used for proper nouns. There may be some use of exclamation marks and question marks. Commas may be used in lists.	*4–5 marks*

Composition and effect

Assessment focuses: Write imaginative, interesting and thoughtful texts. Produce texts which are appropriate to task, reader and purpose. Organise and present whole texts effectively, sequencing and structuring information, ideas and events.

Band	Description	Mark
E1	Some recognisable letters, groups of letters, words or phrases appropriate to the task. The writing needs to be mediated by child, teacher or parent to be understood.	*1 mark*
E2	There is some recognisable information and simple meaning is conveyed through the writing. Vocabulary choices associated with main aspects of the topic (e.g. "race", "winner", "mix", "flour").	*2–3 marks*
E3	Information is generally relevant (e.g. "Remember to turn the oven on before putting in the cake"). Choice of layout is appropriate to the task.	*4–5 marks*
E4	There will be some evidence of viewpoint. Use of headings, line breaks, bullet points or paragraphing. Technical/ambitious vocabulary used. Consistent writing style (e.g. for rules/recipe "You must …", "Do not …", "Remember …", "Always …").	*6–7 marks*

Example Writing for the Short Task – Postcard

Band D Sentence structure and punctuation: Band D3, *4 marks*

Band E Composition and effect: Band E4, *6 marks*

Dear mummy + daddy.

I am Having a good time. I've been Helping Grandpa with his Garden. we've been planting some more potatoes. the wethers been Sunny in the morning and raining in the evening. This is helping Grandpas plants Grow. I am happy with Gran and Grandpa but I am missing you. love you see you soon. James, xxx

Sentence structure and punctuation
Clauses linked by connectives.

Composition and effect
Evidence of viewpoint.

Summary of writing
- Consistent use of appropriate format.

Total marks: 10

Example Writing for the Short Task – Recipe for Making a Cake

Band D Sentence structure and punctuation: Band D1, *1 mark*

Band E Composition and effect: Band E1, *1 mark*

Sentence structure and punctuation
Meaningful words and phrases.

Shans wast
West Put flarnr and Shugr
ten ya a y
teny peint put bee eggs
and to Bake

Composition and effect
Some recognisable letters, words.

Summary of writing

- Writing has to be mediated to be understood.

Total marks: 2

Example Writing for the Short Task – Writing Rules

Band D Sentence structure and punctuation: Band D2, *2 marks*

Band E Composition and effect: Band E4, *6 marks*

Composition and effect
Use of ambitious vocabulary.

Sentence structure and punctuation
Use of "and" to join clauses.

Be patient and Wait your
turn.
run in a Straight line.

always clap evrybody.

Sentence structure and punctuation
Sentences sometimes demarcated by capital letters and full stops.

Summary of writing

- Consistent writing style.
- Use of line breaks.
- Accurate statements used.

Total marks: 8

Handwriting

There is no separate test to assess your child's handwriting. This makes it much easier! A score out of 3 will be given, by assessing the handwriting from the writing tasks.

1 Look at the long and short writing tasks. Choose a few lines where your child has done their best handwriting. This will be the handwriting to assess.

2 Use the table below to match your child's handwriting to a band.

3 Use the examples of children's handwriting on pages 61 and 62. These provide examples of how the writing in different bands may look. Do not worry if your child's handwriting does not exactly match any example. These are only a guide. Use your judgement to find the best fit.

Band	Description	Mark
F1	Writing is legible, letters are usually correctly formed and orientated. Upper and lower case letters are not generally mixed within the word.	*1 mark*
F2	Letters are correctly formed and orientated. Writing shows some evidence of being controlled – letters are generally neat and regular in size. Ascenders and descenders are regular in size.	*2 marks*
F3	Letters are correctly formed and orientated. Handwriting is neat and regular in size. There is evidence of fluency and the ability to join letters.	*3 marks*

Example Handwriting

Example Handwriting – *0 marks*

> Dear Gran and
> Grandpa
> tow day I h wibi vt qaED
> I can qLegy wiLh my cat

Example Handwriting – *1 mark*

> Once upon a time a mouse was
> running across a field and the mous
> met a big cat the cat wanted to
> eat the mouse but the mouse said
> ile race you and ile win. The cat

Example Handwriting – *2 marks*

and there was a bouncy castle and a swimming pool I went in all oss them and the magizene did a skip up and disaperd

Example Handwriting – *3 marks*

Dear Gran and Grandpa,
I'm fine thankyou, how are you?
Are you going to grow anything else in your vegtable patch, such as tomatoes, pears, fruit or anything else.
I'm glad the weather is nice there, but it's so cold here. We have to have the heating, and fire on to make the house warm. She is great, my new teacher, her name's

Spelling Test Passages

Pete's Big Feet

Say "Hi!" to Pete. He is **ever** so sweet.

He is **never** mean and **always** smiles at **people** he meets.

He remembers to say **please** and thank you, too. At **weekends**, Pete likes to help **friends down** his street. He tidies up garden weeds and sweeps floors for them.

When it is sunny, Pete **likes** to fish at Wheat Field Stream.

But his favourite meal is not fish. It is lean meat **with** peas. And if he has a treat, it has to be cheese.

You see, Pete likes the same **things** as **many boys**.

He loves **games** with mates and **seeing** movies. He tries to be neat and tidy in his best **green** jeans.

Above his knees, Pete **looks** like **anyone** you **might** meet. But **below** the knees, he makes some squeal.

"Are those real feet?" some say.

Others ask "Can I have a feel? Wow, **your** feet are unreal!"

You see, Pete has big, no, huge, no, giant-sized feet!

Musical Statues

Instructions on how to play musical statues.

You will **need**:

Music

A stereo

A **place** to **dance**

Lots of **children**

An adult to judge

1. Wait **for** the music to **begin**.
2. **When** the music **starts**, dance around the room.
3. As **soon** as the music **stops**, stand as still as **you** can.
4. Remember not to **move** at all – be **careful** not to blink your **eyes** or **smile**!
5. An adult will **walk** around the room **looking** for anyone who is moving.
6. If you are caught moving, then you are **out** and you must sit at the side of the room.
7. The winner is the last **person** still **dancing**.
8. **Good** luck!

Dear Cinderella

Dear Cinderella,

We are **so** sorry for being horrible to **you** when you lived with us. We **miss** you a lot now that you **live** in the palace with the prince.

We have to do all the cleaning, **washing** and ironing now. It is **just** not fair! The other day our wicked mother **even** made us mop the **floor**.

Last week we had to hang all the washing outside in the **garden** and as soon as we had finished our work it began to rain. We felt very **cross**, especially as our **new** dresses had **been** ruined!

We are both hoping that one **day** we will meet a prince just like you did. When is the prince having **another** ball? We will make sure we wear the most beautiful glass slippers in the whole world.

We would **like** it if you could **come** and visit us sometime because we are quite lonely. We would love to hear all about your new life in the palace. Do you have servants and maids?

Maybe we **should** come and **work** for you one day?

Love **from**

The Ugly **Sisters**

XXX

Using the Spelling Test Score

Your child will have a score out of 20. Use the table below to convert this score into a mark out of 7.

Number of correct words	0–3	4–7	8–11	12–14	15–16	17–18	19–20
Marks	1	2	3	4	5	6	7